The Old Farm

A History of Farming Life in the West Country

ROBIN STANES

DEVON BOOKS

First published in Great Britain in 1990 by Devon Books

CIP Catalogue Record for this book is
available from the British Library

ISBN 0 86114-858-4

Printed and bound in Great Britain by
BPCC Wheatons Ltd, Exeter

DEVON BOOKS

Official Publishers to Devon County Council
An imprint of Wheaton Publishers Ltd. A member of Maxwell
Communication Corporation plc

Wheaton Publishers Ltd
Hennock Road, Marsh Barton, Exeter, Devon EX2 8RP
Tel: 0392 411131; Fax: 0392 425274; Telex 42794 (WHEATN G)

SALES

Direct sales enquiries to Devon Books at the address above.

Photographs

The publishers wish to thank the following for permission to use their photographs: Beaford Archive (plates 4, 5, 6, 11, 14, 16, 18, 22, 23, 24, 25, 26, 29); Dartington Rural Archive (plate 32); Devon Library Services (plates 12, 13, 33); Royal Institution of Cornwall (plates 1, 3, 7, 8, 9, 10, 15, 17, 19, 20, 27, 28, 30, 31); Mr P. H. Gatley (plate 21); James Ravilious (plate 2).

Foreword

TO UNDERSTAND THE PRESENT, we must first understand the past. That is especially true in farming, in which the principles of good husbandry – established by trial and error over the centuries – are as valid now as they ever were.

To understand the landscape, and the nature of the rural communities of the South West, one must also understand the history of the region's agriculture. Why did our predecessors go to such enormous trouble to fence in their fields with great earth banks, topped with thorn and timber? Why should that copse or shelter belt be where it is? Why are the wild moorlands carpeted with heather, instead of being choked with gorse and bracken? In every case, those cherished features of our landscape are simply the by-products of the struggle to produce food and fuel.

A farmer's motivation, first and foremost, is, in the words of Dean Swift, 'to make two blades of grass, or two ears of corn, to grow upon a spot of land where only one grew before'. The desire to improve the production of his farm is in his blood; more than that, it is his reason for existence. But the good farmer is conscious as well that he is but a steward of his land for a short time; that his abiding responsibility is to pass on his land to his successors in a better condition – in every respect – than it was when he took it on. As the old saying has it: 'Live as though you might die tomorrow, but farm as if you would live forever'.

Perhaps sometimes, in the over-regulated, over-complicated, over-publicized farming world of the late twentieth century, we allow ourselves to forget those who came before, and those who will come after. This book puts us in our proper historical context and reminds us that farming means a whole lot more than the latest model of tractor, or the latest government scheme.

Farmers in the South West take an enormous and understandable pride in their achievements in harnessing the earth and the elements to the point where we now produce twice the volume of food that we did before the Second World War. Criticism hurts when you have done what you were asked to do, without – in the farmer's eyes – damaging anyone or anything in the process. Now we are being called upon to change direction; to produce a little less, and in a rather different way. Farmers will respond to the challenge, as they have always done. History teaches us that as well.

Ray Martin
Chairman (1990)
National Farmers Union

Acknowledgements

Many people have contributed to what I have written. I must mention a few: Arthur and Hazel Ellis, Oliver Pears, Bill Dale, Leslie Farmiloe, Reg Leatherland, Ted Evans, Albert Fisher, George Chappell, Fred Lane, Tom King, George Walker, Jack and Ivy Squire, Arthur Madge, Douglas Rowland, Don White, Edwin and Betty Johns, Janet Passmore, Brian Clist, Dick Wills, Freda Wilkinson, Elizabeth Gawne, Kay Coutin, Hermon French, Philip Jenkinson, Harold Fox, Charles Hulland, Michael Havinden, Peter Beacham and the Rev Dr John Powell. It has been a privilege and a pleasure to listen to them all. Peter Hunt, the Amenities and Countryside Officer at Devon County Council, has given me immense encouragement and assistance throughout the writing of the book.

I also wish to acknowledge help from the Devon County Record Office, The Beaford Archive, The Dartington Archive, The Royal Institution of Cornwall, The Museum of English Rural Life (Reading), the Torquay Museum and the Alscott Farm Museum.

This book is dedicated to Clemency.

CONTENTS

Introduction   7

Part I: The Farmhouse

  1. A Good Farm   9

  2. The Development of the Farmhouse   13

  3. Inside the Farmhouse   25

  4. Food   53

  5. Drink   61

Part II: Farm Work

  6. 'The Best Husbandry'   73

  7. The Fields of the Farm   76

  8. 'Mighty Great Hedges'   100

  9. Ploughing and Tilling   107

10. Sowing the Seed   120

11. Corn Harvest   127

12. Haymaking   134

13. Livestock   140

14. The Farmyard   148

Part III: Farm Life

15. The Family and the Farm   153

16. Society and Religion   162

17. Fun and Festivals   169

Bibliography   173

Introduction

IN 1952 I HAD LAMBING ewes on the farm on 'half crease'. That meant that I had the ewes for a year. I tended to them, I lambed them, and at the end of the year I had the value of all the wool and half the lambs. The owner of the ewes was the late Arthur Ellis of Pittaford, a great sheep man, who lived for, and in fact died amongst his sheep. He came originally from the edges of Dartmoor and the breed he kept (and loved and judged) was the Dartmoor Greyface. I learnt an immense amount about sheep from him. If there was any problem, he would come over, and almost invariably sort it out. He liked a joke, and I can recall great guffaws of laughter one day when he found me defending myself from an irate and vicious Suffolk ram that he had wished on me at tupping time.

One of his ewes that I looked after one year would not 'take' her lamb but butted it away when it tried to suck. The lamb was getting weaker and so Arthur came over. The ewe and her lamb were in a smallish pen; Arthur recognized her as having reared a lamb well enough the year before. Whatever we did, she still wouldn't love the lamb. 'Get the dog in', he said. I had no idea what he was about, but duly got my dog into the pen. The immediate reaction of the ewe was to defend her lamb against the dog, to protect it and love it. Fear of the dog, mother love, overcame her rejection, and that did the trick. The ewe raised her lamb well. Some years later I was reading casually in Fitzherbert's *Book of Husbandry*, written about 1530, and found that Fitzherbert gave the same advice to his readers as Arthur Ellis gave to me, and Arthur had certainly never read or heard of Fitzherbert. This advice may be read on page 145 in this book.

It came to me then, and later, that in the 1950s I was still just part of, and sharing in, the tail end of an ancient traditional way of life that was centuries and maybe millenia old. Farmers were still then using horses, still making hay stacks and corn ricks and thatching them, still cutting and laying hedges and making up banks, still milking by hand, often sitting beside a great fireplace and cooking on an open fire, still raising cream and killing a pig regularly to cure and salt, still eating fat bacon and making and drinking cider, cutting the ashen faggot at Christmas, and drawing water from a well. All of these customs and practices were immemorial. Farmers still grew mangolds and swedes as they had been doing for a couple of centuries, and getting in the threshing machine to thresh their ricks as they had been doing for eighty or ninety years. The combine was only just taking over. Everyone had a tractor but they were new; a few used the electric fence; silage was still suspect; old farm buildings still served a useful farming purpose; poultry were kept in twenties and thirties and scratched about in the farmyard, instead of by thousands in a battery; pigs by the dozen instead of by hundreds. A dairy herd was large if it was thirty strong, instead of today's one hundred and fifty. All that has changed almost entirely, and this book is an attempt to recall and reveal something of that life from personal memories, from talking to and listening to farmers and farm workers, and from moderately extensive reading and some research.

The book's geographical scope is the West Country. By this is meant Cornwall, Devon and the western parts of Somerset and Dorset which make up the south-western peninsula. Most of it is within what geographers call the highland zone of Britain. East of this the peninsula, farming practice seems to have been different in many ways. Indeed William Marshall, the acute reporter of farming practice at the end of the eighteenth century, considered the peninsula's agriculture so different as to seem to belong to another country. From the Quantocks and Blackdowns westwards to Land's End, farming life and farming economy had a certain common character. This book will examine that character and explain some of its details.

The principal written sources I have used have been as follows. William Marshall wrote *The Rural Economy of the West of England* in 1796. This deals with Devon and Cornwall. Marshall also wrote accounts of the farming of other counties and managed the estate at Buckland Abbey for some years. In 1809 Charles Vancouver, a Hampshire man, wrote his detailed *General View of the Agriculture of Devon* for the Board of Agriculture. For Cornwall, George Worgan, a schoolmaster and leaseholder of Liskeard, did much the same survey in 1809. In 1667 Samuel Colepresse wrote his *Georgicall account of Devon and Cornwall* answering a detailed questionaire for the Royal Society. Colepresse was an FRS and Rector of Plympton and a keen observer of his local scene. Around 1750, another clergyman, the Dean of Exeter, Jeremiah Milles, sent out enquiries to all the parishes in Devon with the intention of writing a history of the county. A number of enquiries related to farming and these were often answered by the parson or the schoolmaster. This is the Milles' MS. Another source of information for, mainly, the seventeenth century, comes from inventories of men's and women's goods and stock, most containing farming information, which were made in order to help prove their wills. Those few that survive for Devon have been edited and transcribed by Margaret Cash in *Devon Inventories*. Finally, Professor H. P. R. Finberg used the extensive collection of Tavistock Abbey documents to write *Tavistock Abbey*. This has a valuable chapter on monastic farming in Devon in the late fifteenth and early sixteenth century. A more detailed list of sources can be found in the bibliography.

Part I:
The Farmhouse

1.
A Good Farm

IN THE PAST, FARMHOUSES AND yards were built first and foremost where there was a good spring of water or a never failing well. Apart from his own needs, a man had to have water for his animals and in the past no farm was without oxen or horses to pull the plough. A good stream or spring was one that ran or 'welled up' in abundance all the year round, even in September and October, when levels were at their lowest, just before the winter rains broke. In the South West, water is seldom very far from the surface: wells, where they exist, are usually shallow, but on the limestone, as at Bovey House near Beer, elaborate arrangements in the form of a man-powered wheel, had to be made to pull up water from great depths. A good water supply made for a good farm; land without water had to be used for crops or for sheep, which drink little except in very dry weather.

Water had other uses. From quite early days techniques were developed to irrigate valley bottoms and even dry hillsides by a network of contour furrows. This extended the grazing season and provided abundant lush early grass in the spring to feed ewes and lambs. Water also provided power for water wheels in both mills and farms that could do a number of useful jobs. In Payhembury in 1809, a Mr Venn had a wheel that thrashed, winnowed, ground corn, crushed apples and shelled clover seed.

With good water available, the next consideration for siting a farm might be the availability of building materials. Old farmhouses were often built from the rock or earth on which they stood. Stone and cob are the most common materials and these could often be dug on site. Cob is principally subsoil mixed with straw and water. Almost all Devon subsoils can be used to make good cob, and out of this the farmhouse and the farm buildings were constructed layer by layer, using the labour of the farmer and his men. Villages built in this way and left without roughcast or whitewash to conceal the native colour of the loam, were, it was remarked, impossible to distinguish at a distance from a burning stubble field, 'both having uniformly the same shade, and from both of which smoke arises'.

Stone, particularly cut prepared stone, ashlar, was much more expensive. It could sometimes be picked up from the land, as on Dartmoor or near a quarry, or even dug precisely where the house was to stand. Many farmhouses can be seen to stand on a shelf or in a dip where earth or stone with which to build it has been dug. The roof could be grown on the farm. In the country, thatch was usual using rye or wheat straw, combed to make what was known as 'reed'. Farmers or their men all thatched ricks and most could manage a not too elegant house roof as well. Timbers for the roof came from hedgerow trees, or from village woodland, and the spars for thatching came from the annual cutting of the hedges. The village saw pit could shape the trusses, the blacksmith could fashion the ironwork, and the carpenter make the doors and windows. Once the right site had been chosen a man could, with the help of his neighbours, build his own house and roof it from materials grown on the farm.

In the South West it was normal for a man's land to surround his farm, to lie in a ring fence. Elsewhere, for example in Midland England, a farmer's land lay dispersed in strips in the open fields, but this system was largely gone in the South West by the seventeenth century. Up until the nineteenth century there were some big villages, Otterton, Broadhembury, Ugborough, for example, where the farmhouses lay in the village street and the land was arranged into a sort of open field, but this was fairly rare. Instead, a landscape of small, hedged fields of three to four acres had been created around each farm, very much as can be seen to-day. This land, sometimes growing crops, sometimes under grass, needed to be well drained, not too steep or stony, south-facing and 'early' with perhaps a little land 'back-sun' (that is, facing north) to stay green in a drought. At best, land neatly surrounded his farm, so that from near his farmyard a man might survey at a glance all his fields and crops and stock.

The most valuable land was meadow. This lay along the banks of streams and would be damp in the driest summers. It would grow the all-essential hay to feed the oxen that ploughed the corn fields which fed the village folk. Even in Domesday Book meadow land was five or six times the value of arable. It was rarely ploughed, unlike the rest of the land, but could produce early grass from watering. Good meadow was treasured, and it took long years to build a good sward. 'To make a pasture breaks a man', was an old Midland saying. However, if it was ever ploughed it cropped wonderfully, so the saying concluded: 'To break [plough] a pasture makes a man'. Often meadow was created out of marshy valley bottoms by draining. Purfleet, or Poffitt, in Payhembury, now a lush meadow, means 'wet land [fleet] where the bittern [pur] lives'. Bitterns like wet rushy fen. Once drained, this wet land could be of great value.

By regulated flooding, the flat land on valley bottoms could be turned into water meadows, to promote early growth of grass. Farmers in upland Devon adapted this practice by converting hillsides into 'catch meadows'. These were created by digging parallel contour furrows at regular intervals up and along the slope of a hilly field. These were fed with water from a stream that rose much further up the valley and this was led, often through a farmyard to collect manure, sometimes to a small dammed pool or sometimes direct into each furrow in turn. These were dammed at their ends and the water overflowed and watered the land down to the next furrow, creating lush green growth, mainly for ewes and their lambs that did not 'poach' the soil and needed green grass to stimulate milk supply.

Watering began in October once the springs were replenished by autumn rains and continued till February or March when grass began to shoot naturally. There was a lot of labour involved in maintaining the furrows and directing the water but green grass in February or March, the hungry gap, was invaluable. The remains of such meadows can be seen all over the South West as faint parallel lines in hillside fields. Some were still in use until the 1950s.

Pasture was another necessity. This, in the South West, meant rough pasture, upland grazing, in contrast to the Midland meaning. Almost every parish had some hilly common pasture on which cattle and sheep could be grazed in summer, out of the buzz of flies. This would save the inland grass fields on the farm itself for hay. Furze (gorse) faggots could be cut on the common, and 'vags' or turves, dug for firing. It could be used to summer cattle and sheep, and in the winter wet, such land could stand heavy poaching by cattle. Exmoor, Dartmoor, Bodmin Moor and the other upland commons were all used in these ways by farmers, often living many miles away. A farm with common rights was essentially a rather bigger farm than its stated acreage indicated, and indeed some farms had rough land like this within their own fence, to be ploughed and cropped as the need arose.

In the hilly South West there were steep inaccessible corners that were best left as woodland. This was never neglected or wasted. If it was coppiced, cut to the ground every fifteen years or so, it would provide some of the essential firewood for the kitchen fire. Faggots of firewood were very saleable and there was always a need for wood for posts, handles and hurdles. Building timber was obtained from the larger trees which were felled according to a system of husbandry that regarded timber as a renewable resource. Occasionally charcoal might be burnt, or oaks stripped for tanbarking. In the past, pigs rooted for beech mast and cattle grazed the young shoots, and both sheep and cattle found shelter in driving weather.

Water, building materials, arable land, meadow, pasture, and woodland were all important in the siting of a farm. Probably least important was the view from the farmhouse, though many farms in the South West occupy delightful sites, tucked into 'a heal', a hollow, in the slope of a hill, with their arable and meadow below. Farmers were practical men, with little taste for aesthetics. When asked to admire an idyllic view over woods and fields, one old man said: 'All I see is work'.

There were, of course, other matters to be considered when siting the farmhouse. Old houses were cold: the only source of heat might be the one kitchen log fire kept permanently alight. Chimneys were huge: without a draught they smoked; with one, the warmest place was on a high backed settle tight to the fire. To attract a bit more warmth, most houses faced south and were often backed closely into the slope of the hill. Trees, the tough sycamore and, later, pines, provided shelter from the wind, but few tenant farmers thought it worthwhile looking after what was often landlords' property. More important was level ground for the house and the farmyard, which needed to be close to the house for tending the stock. A good south-east facing, late-flowering site for the farm cider orchard was also a consideration. No farm could be without cider in the past. Access was unimportant and could be down a 'sticklepath', a lane wide enough for one horse, probably leading through the muck of the farmyard. How the house looked was also probably quite unimportant, a purely practical matter, until wealth increased, and folk became conscious of status. Yeomen, the richer farmers, took to embellishing their houses according to the prevalent taste, but the husbandmen, the poorer tiller of the soil, could not afford such niceties, and his house makes that plain.

2.
The Development of the Farmhouse

FARMERS LIVED WHERE THEY WORKED; the farmhouse was at once a home and a place of work. It needed to be big enough to house not only the farmer and his family but also the servants and apprentices who milked the cows, fed the pigs, ploughed the fields, cleaned out the shippons, laid the hedges and carried out all the innumerable daily chores, both agricultural and domestic, that could only be done by hand. A good-sized farmhouse a hundred years ago might have a dozen or more inhabitants, all eating at the same board and sleeping sometimes three or four to an upstairs room or quite commonly above a shippon or stable. All these were 'family' in the old sense of the word; they lived and ate together but the farmer and his wife and children had automatic precedence, the better seats at the kitchen table and the better sleeping chambers within the house. Most farmhands lived in their master's house until they married and marriage was often put off to a late age until some sort of separate dwelling became available.

A farmer, a husbandman, tilled his land and nurtured his livestock to provide himself and his family with the means to live. That was the first call on his time and energy. But there has probably never been a time when, even on the smallest farm, there was not something to sell, a surplus of wool or grain or butter or cheese or whatever the season had favoured. Almost all farmers were tenants who had an obligation of rent to pay every year, so most farmers' inventories taken on their death show 'money in his purse'. There were also blacksmiths' bills to pay, new stock or seed had to be purchased occasionally and new cloam tableware had to be bought, annually, at the local fair. Then there were the luxuries: tea or coffee, when they became usual; ribbons and lace and a new hat or two; a bottle of brandy and a plug of tobacco. These needed cash. Some of the other needs could be met by barter 'across the hedge' by a favour done or by a day or two's work or by some cautious exchange but there was always a certain need for money. In the main, however, the economy of the farm was probably not a money economy; most of a man's efforts were directed towards self-sufficiency. His food and drink were home made or home produced and all the work entailed by this was done on the farm.

Much of the necessary work for preparing and preserving food was done in the farm kitchen and, besides that, large farm houses had a great many specialist rooms: dairies, cheese rooms or wring houses, still rooms, smoking chambers, butteries for the butts or barrels, apple cellars, and malt chambers. Many farmers' wives spun yarn and wove cloth for both their own use or for sale and room had to be found for all this activity. As close as possible were the shippons, calf houses, pigsties and fowl houses, cared for frequently by the womenfolk, while the men worked the horses or oxen, ploughed and hedged and did the hard manual work. Such was the farmhouse and farmstead at its most developed, before mechanization made a large staff unnecessary and the concepts of privacy and status banished the farmworkers to the tied cottage.

In medieval times some farmhouses in the West Country provided one large main room, the hall, in the centre of which there was a fire (fig. 1). On this the food was cooked, and around it the family as a whole slept at night with very few concessions to privacy. This basic house plan probably has the same origin as the Saxon hall, a huge communal rectangular living house with a central hearth that can be dated back at the very least to pre-Conquest times. In this, at its greatest and most magnificent, royalty lived, but the same plan was used all down the social scale. At the lowest peasant level a shippon or cattle house, where the oxen were housed, very frequently formed an integral part of the house. Plough oxen needed to be well housed as they provided the motive power to plough the land, and were probably the farmer's most prized possessions and the familiar companions of many days work. They added their warmth to that of the fire hearth and their closeness made the milking of the cows and the necessary attention easy. Folk even thought that milking cows needed the sight and warmth of the fire to milk well. This type of house, where animals and people lived under the same roof, is known as the 'longhouse' and it is one of the earliest house types in the West Country. More sophisticated (and today much altered) longhouses can still be seen on or near Dartmoor. Houses of a similar ground plan with two, three or more rooms in a line, but none of which ever housed cattle, are often (but, strictly speaking, incorrectly) called longhouses too. The farmhouse with three rooms in a line and a cross passage became the most common type in Devon and other parts of the West Country.

In its basic form the longhouse is of two rooms divided by a cross passage. To one side of the passage ('above') was the hall where there was a fire and where the men and women lived. On the other side of the passage ('below') were the cattle in their shippon, heads to the outside walls and a dung channel between them with a drain hole at the lower end. Longhouses were more often than not built lengthwise down a gentle slope and this helps to explain the use of the words above and below the passage. Cattle and men shared the same entrance into the passage with a wall or a screen on the upper side through which a door entered the hall. On the lower side the entrance to the shippon was often open. Frequently there was a

Fig. 1.
Cooking at a
reredos on an
open hearth.
This is on
display at
St Fagan's
Museum,
Cardiff.

door at the further end of the passage leading to a backyard ('backlet') with outbuildings. Here cattle could be separated if need be. There was, it seems, nothing wrong in these early days for men and cattle to share the same entrance with all the mud and dung to be negotiated. In later houses two entrances were inserted to separate man and beast. Above the shippon, where the cattle lay, hay could be stored in the roof space. Along each wall of the shippon there were mangers and feeding passages. To these the cattle were tied with a cunningly constructed home-made halter made of springy willow or nutwood. Here the cows were milked and calves were born, so close to the farmer's hall that the lowing and stirring of the cattle could be easily heard.

'Above' the passage, life in the hall was warmer and cleaner. In the middle of the hall was the hearth, a paved circle of stone where the fire was kept burning continuously. There was no chimney. At best smoke rose eventually through a hole in the roof which was lined with boarding to create something of a cowl-like construction. This did not exclude the rain entirely and was not a certain way of getting rid of the smoke, so that the whole hall was often smoke filled. Chaucer's widow lived in such a hall 'full sooty was her bower and eke her hall'. She had, at least, two rooms and her livestock were outside. Two centuries later, a poor man's house, where there was only one room and nothing to separate the farmer from his livestock, was described thus by Bishop Hall:

> Of one bay's breadth God wot a silly cote,
> Whose thatched spars are furred with sluttish soot,
> A whole inch thick shining like blackmore's brows,
> Through smoke that down the headless barrel blows,
> At his bed's head feeden his stallen teame,·
> His swine beneath, his pullen o'er the beam.

A good husbandman would see to it that he had really dry wood that gave a more or less smokeless fire but in many existing houses soot blackening and indeed soot can still be found in the apex of the roof where once there was once 'a headless barrel'.

In this sort of house the farmer, his family and servants slept round the fire, perhaps on mattresses filled with chaff or douse as it was called in the South West. There seem to have been no concessions to the idea of privacy initially; the most primitive houses show no separate room and of course no bedrooms upstairs. Children must then have been conceived and born more or less in public, though there were perhaps screens or hangings to create temporary privacy. From a fairly early date another room was added above the hall that came to be known as the solar – perhaps because it provided some solitude – or the bower, or much later the parlour. Both the function of this room, and its name, clearly varied with time and the status of the owner; it may well have often been a store house for the more valuable possessions of the farmer. It seems probable that medieval houses did have some sort of screening within the hall, perhaps six or seven feet high, but whether these were used right down the social scale is uncertain and they would have had to accommodate the central hearth which was the only way of heating until the sixteenth century. People with quite high status lived in quite small houses. In Monmouthshire it has been shown that a man acknowledged as a 'gentleman' lived in a hall only eighteen feet in length with all his family and servants. This house had a solar or separate room. The so called manor house at the excavated medieval village of Houndtor has three rooms. The other houses on the site are more modest and have only two rooms.

The oldest farmhouses were all single-storey buildings. The presence of the hearth in the middle of the floor and the absence of any chimney to take out the smoke made an upper floor impractical. Chimneys started to appear in ordinary houses probably towards the end of the fifteenth century, though their appearance in Devon may be later. William Harrison, a parson from Essex, wrote in his *Description of England* (1580):

> There are old men yet dwelling in the village where I remain which have noted three things to be marvellously altered in England within their sound remembrance; one is the multitude of chimnies lately erected whereas in their young days there were not above two or three, if so many, in most uplandish towns of the realm.

Medieval great houses, castles and monasteries had chimneys as Harrison noted. These were built within the thickness of, or added to, a wall. It is odd that this idea was not adopted sooner in the much smaller house. Possibly it was a matter of expense; only a stone chimney was really safe. Cob chimneys became quite common in poorer houses, but they were dangerous; rat or mouse holes in the cob allowed sparks to reach the dry underside of the thatch.

Once a chimney was built on to the house in the passage wall or against a side wall, a first floor could be inserted. Houses then ceased to have a 'hall' in the old sense, though for a long time the name was kept for the most important room, often the room near the entry door. Open halls survived in the West Country well into the seventeenth century and some examples still exist. However, the sixteenth century saw a very general insertion of first floors and the development of chambers and upper rooms, eventually to be themselves heated with a separate fireplace: a real sign of wealth. Many present houses can be seen to have had an open hall by an examination of the underside of the ridge beam and its surrounding purlins and rafters. If these are smoke blackened then the house was once open to the roof, with an open fire.

It would be a mistake to suggest that no attempts were made to improve the old hall as described above (fig. 2). Before the advent of the wall chimney there were attempts to insert floors to create upper rooms. The solar or bower could be roofed over and a partition inserted to the roof to separate it from the open hall. This was often jettied out into the hall to provide a sort of canopy at one end, sometimes above the master's place at table. This space could be used for storage or as a bed chamber. Much the same could be done at the lower end of the hall above the cross passage and the room 'below' the passage, again perhaps jettied out, so that both ends, but not the middle of the house, were of two stories. Upper chambers were reached initially by a simple ladder inserted in a hole in the floor but this gave place to all sorts of more elaborate staircases. Circular newel stairs were sometimes built in the thickness of the wall or a wooden stair constructed from the cross passage or from elsewhere in the house. The old comic name for the staircase was 'the timberen hill'.

The majority of farmhouses were 'ceiled' by the late sixteenth century or totally rebuilt with a first floor. It was once believed that there was a 'great rebuilding' in the late sixteenth century when, with increasing prosperity, old medieval houses were knocked down and replaced. William Harrison has some words on this:

> Every man almost is a builder, he that hath bought any small parcel of ground will not be quiet till he have pulled down the old house and set up a new after his own device...It is a world to see how diverse men being bent to building and in spending of their goods in that trade, daily imagine new devices of their own to guide their workman withal...In the proceeding of their works how they set up, how they pull down, how they add to, how they take from, whereby their heads are never idle, their purses never shut nor their books of account ever made perfect.

Despite these words, which may be most applicable to Harrison's part of the world, it seems likely that 'rebuilding' is the wrong word in the South West and that 'remodelling' or 'renewel' would be more appropriate, and that a great many houses are in fact medieval, dating in their walls and roof from the fifteenth century or earlier. Any house with smoke-blackened roof timbers dates almost certainly from the mid sixteenth century at the latest. It would be interesting to know when exactly the last hall house was constructed, and when the first new upper-storey house was built. At a guess, rural conservatism being what it is, hall houses continued to be built long after the first 'modern' upper-storey house was constructed. Most old houses show a continuous series of changes and additions and modifications as taste and status and wealth and technique dictated; that is part of their charm. There cannot be many old rural houses which were built all at once, say, in 1623, though that date may appear on a prominent date stone. The date may only refer to a major alteration. The change from hall house to an upper-storey house certainly reflects a demand for higher standards of comfort and privacy but it may also reflect a change in society. It made it possible to banish the servants to another part of the house at least to sleep and perhaps to eat, and from this beginning the parlour, the withdrawing room, and the servants hall eventually emerge as part and parcel of the middle-class house in the eighteenth and nineteenth centuries. Gentlemen often liked to preserve their halls, they became symbols of status, and they could afford to add servants' quarters to the old house. Farmers, on the other hand, who worked necessarily with their farm and house servants, could not be quite so class-conscious and ate as 'family', probably until this century, though the servants still slept where they could, above the cows or in an attic, often four or five to a room, and two or three to a bed.

Construction

Some early fifteenth- and early sixteenth-century houses in the South West are cruck houses (fig. 3). This term describes the method of roof construction and can be used fairly crudely as a means of dating. True cruck houses have the main trusses of the roof, the principal weight bearing members, made of single unjoined lengths of timber, most commonly oak. By Harrison's time everyone was building in oak. 'Never so much oak hath been spent in a hundred years before as in ten years of our time...In times past men were contented to dwell in houses built of sallow, willow, plum tree, hornbeam and elm now nothing but oak is in any whit regarded'. He could not resist adding 'when our houses were builded of willow then had we oken men, now that our houses be made of oke our men are not only become willow, but a great many altogether straw'.

True crucks rise from a plinth of stone, often no more than a couple of feet from ground level, in an uninterrupted curve to the ridge of the roof. Often the two crucks of a truss are a matching pair, sawn longitudinally from the trunk and a branch of an oak that was probably felled for the purpose. A two-bay house like that of Chaucer's widow needed three rightly shaped trees from the manor wood. The length of the pairs of crucks determined the depth of the house and it is most unusual for an original house to be more than one room thick or more than about eighteen feet in depth. Any greater depth demanded very lengthy trees, which were probably very rare, and some sort of internal framework, such as the hammer beam and wind braces, to support the great weight and span of the roof. Cruck trusses seem to have been prefabricated by builders and stored ready for use; an act of Henry VIII's reign forbade the secret burning of frames of timber ready to be set up and edified as houses. Cruck houses built in this way could be taken down and re-erected elsewhere without much difficulty.

At its smallest, an early house could be roofed, as prehistoric huts normally were, with short lengths of timber from a hedgerow, giving a depth of ten or twelve feet and a very low and smoky roof for the hall. Almost certainly, the erection of a cruck house was a communal affair. Barn raising in the days of the early settlement of America was done communally, using easily-available local timber to deal with a similar problem of construction. The truss would be cut out and joined with tie beams on the ground, and raised on a stone plinth by concerted manpower to a position where the purlins could be pegged into place between truss and truss. Early purlins were threaded through purpose-cut holes in the truss, so this was not so simple. Once all the trusses and the ridge piece were in place and the whole propped at either end, the neighbours could go home and leave the rest to the proud owner. He had to build up stone or cob walls between the trusses, and at both ends, and wherever else solid dividing walls were required. Then he had to peg on the rafters and battening, and thatch the house with reed or straw, or sometimes heather.

Cruck building continued until and into the seventeenth century but

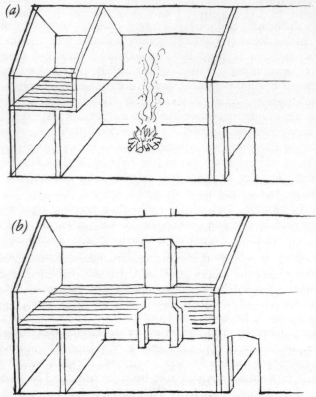

Fig. 2. The development of the house:
(a) an open hall with jettied chamber
(b) fireplace and ceiling inserted

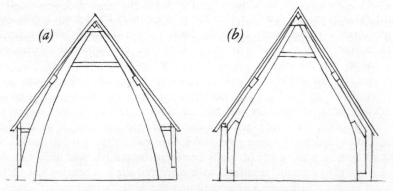

Fig. 3. Two types of cruck construction:
(a) true crucks (b) jointed crucks

it became much modified. Long-enough timber seems to have become unobtainable or too expensive, and probably the first change was to introduce the jointed cruck, where two lengths of timber were morticed and pegged together to reach the required length. This was less strong, but became the most common way of roofing in much of the South West. In most examples the 'foot', the bottom section, was raised a considerable height off ground level. Next, the cruck became much shorter, the half cruck. This was mounted on the top of a stone or cob wall just below where the roof proper began. The last development was to abandon the cruck altogether and to use instead an A-frame truss set on the very top of the exterior walls. This is the more recent 'traditional' roof in the West Country.

Crucks were curved but the walls of the house needed to be upright. Inside a cruck house the base of the cruck can often be seen bending inwards from the vertical wall and curving towards the ridge. This can be even more marked at first-floor level where the cruck may emerge from the floor some distance from the outside wall to reach the ceiling close to the line of the roof. It is likely that most true cruck houses were originally hall houses. Sometimes the crucks are chamfered and decorated, even though this elaboration can only be seen now from a first-floor room. In such a case the house was certainly a hall house, since such finish was designed to be seen, to grace the best room in the house.

Outside walls in the ordinary West Country farmhouse were of stone or cob. Timber framed exterior walls, so common in much of the rest of Midland and Southern England, are quite absent from the South West, except in towns. Dartmouth, Totnes, Exeter and Plymouth are rich with fine, timber, merchants' houses, but for no clear reason they are quite absent from the countryside. Interior walls were often of simple timber-framing, filled with reed or timber laths and plastered-stud work. A common but more expensive feature of many Devon farmhouses was an elaborate joined wooden-pannelled screen in the cross passage or dividing two rooms.

Building exterior walls in cob was not difficult. Cob is made from subsoil mixed with straw. The subsoil is dug from the site of construction and mixed with straw and water. This is most easily done by the treading of cattle or donkeys, though it can laboriously be trodden by men. The relatively small feet of cattle and their greater weight per square inch tread the cob into a cohesive sticky mass. This is put up on a two foot stone or brick plinth by eye when still wet. A plumb line is used, but no shuttering, and the rough strawy edges are shaved off with a hay knife or cranked chopping axe. About two to three feet can be put up safely at one time and then the cob must be left to dry for two or three weeks before the next layer can be raised. The process of building a house of cob was, however, probably more or less continuous, since the first lengths of wall were probably dry enough by the time the end had been reached. Cob needs drying weather, though not necessarily dry weather, to cure; so it is said that a cob building should be begun when the birds start building their nests and finish by the time they lose their feathers. Windows and doors were incorporated in the cob using a wooden framework to create the necessary gaps.

Cob is more or less indestructible if it is kept dry, though the edges will become dusty unless covered up with plaster. In consistency it is a bit like a lump of sugar; sections can be removed or cut out without any danger of collapse, and cob walls will stand for centuries with cracks and holes quite unacceptable in other materials. It has a pleasing rounded appearance without too many straight lines or right angles. It has, somehow, a human dimension in that it not clinically and coldly perfect. It can of course be made to look perfect; many four-square, rectangular, seemingly Victorian houses turn out, if a patch of plaster is removed, to be good solid cob beneath. Cob is undateable; it, or something like it, has probably always been in use, but its nature ensures that it does not survive for the archaeologist's trowel. Ruined cob houses quickly become one with the soil from which they seem at times to have grown. It was a common material where there was no cheap stone or timber. Not only was it the obvious material for a poor man wishing to build his own house, but it was used for the largest farmhouses. Its use is not confined to the South West; something like it was used all over the country and in Brittany and Normandy it was common: the French word is *torchis*. Cob houses were still being built in this century, and some cob building still goes on today.

Later changes in the house

The three-roomed, cross-passage plan became the standard farmhouse type and continued in use for many years. The great 'rebuilding' or 'remodelling' seems to have been complete by the end of the seventeenth century and not too many new or renewed farm houses built to the old plan can be found dating from the eighteenth.

This century in the South West, as elsewhere, saw the decline of the small farmer, the husbandman, and the emergence of the yeoman and the labourer as the two predominant figures in farming society. This is reflected in their houses. Old farm houses lining the village street tended to become labourers' cottages. They were partitioned and a new door provided for each house. Often the original single structure of the roof survives above a whole row of small cottages to show that once this was a single farmhouse. Such an arrangement can be very clearly seen in Broadhembury, in east Devon. Some of these rows may have been built as labourers' cottages from the beginning but this was probably unusual. Few West Country farmers farmed on the scale needed to bear that kind of expense and the tradition was to have a good many living-in farm servants. It was probably easier to use an old farmhouse surplus to needs, as farms became fewer and larger. Some of these old houses were no more than rural slums, with leaky roofs of rotting thatch, windows with shutters only and no glass, damp and dark and dirty. Such a cottage or house modernized and heated is much in demand today, but in the last century some labourers' cottages were so appalling that the Rector of Halberton, the famous Canon Girdlestone, accused the local farmers of housing their cattle better than their men. Farmers probably preferred to get out of the village street and live in a house on their own land, where possible. Some great houses that had been abandoned by the family as too old fashioned or too expensive to put in order also became the homes of labourers. The Pellews' great house at Old Canonteign was occupied by labourers' families before the last war and the remains of the Martins' 'manor house' at Combe Martin was a labourer's house in the nineteenth century.

As farms became bigger there was a need to enlarge the farmhouse. This was done in all sorts of ways. A wing could be added at front or back, or even two wings, as at Hayes Barton in East Budleigh. Early wings often contained the new parlour. A porch and porch room above could be elegantly fitted on to the front. Often these have date stones which commemorate the date of the porch rather than that of the house. A simple addition was to extend the line of the roof at the back to create a 'lean-to' that could house a scullery or dairy. These, however, are sometimes part of the original building as the uniform continuous masonry of the side wall may reveal. Sometimes these lean-tos ran the whole length of the house and incorporated small upper rooms. These are known as linhay rooms in Cornwall and hence this type of house is known as a linhay house. Houses could either be built or rebuilt in this way fairly simply. Occasionally the house was turned round and the old original house became the wing while a new front, of brick or ashlar perhaps, with a good elevation and sash windows, was built to present a more sophisticated gentrified face to the world. The most obvious and commonest addition was merely to lengthen the house at either end. This can sometimes be detected from a change in the roofline.

All these changes were additions or embellishments to the basic vernacular tradition of the three-roomed cross-passage house. Perhaps the first break from this tradition came in the form of the double-pile house, in effect two narrow houses built together lengthwise with separate roof structures. This made it possible to have much larger rooms since the depth of the house could be doubled without having recourse to the elaborate braced and strutted roof. Both 'piles' could be newly built or one might be the old house with the new 'pile' at front or back. Later the A-frame roof was developed, without any obvious difficulties, to cover both piles.

Eventually quite a new style of house was evolved. This is what might best be described as the 'villa' farmhouse, with a central door, four or five windows symmetrically arranged around that door, each lighting a single room, and a chimney on each gable end. This elevation matches exactly a child's immediate instinctive drawing of a house today; a sixteenth-century child would have had a different image. These houses began to be built at the end of the eighteenth and the beginning of the nineteenth century. They were still purpose-built farmhouses with a slated kitchen and dairy, and the building materials used, local rubble stone or cob and slate, were still in the vernacular tradition. Sometimes a covering of stucco, plaster, concealed rubble stone work or cob. Inside, the plan was four-square, a room at each corner on both floors with a central stair and a servants' stair leading out of the kitchen to the servants' attic bedrooms. Although they were functionally farmhouses they marked a complete change from the vernacular tradition of the past. It is not clear why this took place. Apart from the necessary landing, these houses are no bigger or more practical than the old style, nor do they make the separation of 'them', the servants, from 'us' any easier, though they do away completely with the hearth in the kitchen, or hall as the focus of the house. At first glance it seems to have been a matter of fashion and style, a reflection of the contemporary classical style in greater houses. This is a far cry from the originally pure practicalities of the old layout. But a good many of these houses may have been landlord's building, built in fact by an estate owner for a tenant and reflecting landlords' tastes and ideas. In contrast, until probably the end of the eighteenth century, the farmhouse seems to have been the responsibility of the tenant, to build and alter and repair as he wished. This was done using landlords' materials – timber and stone – and was occasionally aided financially by concessions of rent.

The great rebuilding or remodelling was stimulated by a desire for better living conditions and financed by prosperity. The sixteenth and early seventeenth centuries were good times for farmers with vastly rising prices for their corn and wool and wages static by comparison. Wool and cloth financed fine churches like Tiverton and Cullompton, schools like Blundells, bridges like Bideford Bridge. In every parish in Devon and Cornwall there are or were a dozen or more good substantial, sometimes fine houses dating from the sixteenth and seventeenth century, all built largely by farmers out of the profits of the land. It was indeed the land 'that paid for all'. Again in the nineteenth century, land provided for a century or so wealth for landowners and a good living at least for the larger tenant farmers. Rural society also changed, the many small farmers and husbandmen gave place to the yeoman and farm labourer. The farmhouse reflects all these changes admirably. Today the old farmhouse has often become too big and difficult for a farmer's wife, without help of any kind and no servants in the house. The farmer himself runs two or three hundred acres with the help perhaps of his son or of one man who lives, possibly in a council house, some miles away, and drives to work. So the farmer lives in a bungalow and he is often more of a technician and business man than a 'husbandman'. The old house has been sold, often to 'foreigners' who fancy an old and elegant house full of character for their retirement, or from whence they may commute; the barns can be converted into further expensive houses. This development has been brought about largely by technology applied to the working of the farm and to the bringing of once remote areas in touch with urban life. The farmhouse is hardly any longer the home and the place of work for the farming family, which lives largely off the land. This marks an enormous change, the end of a way of life that was centuries, if not millenia old.

3.
Inside the Farmhouse

Chambers and bedrooms

The creation of two full floors where one had been before, the sealing (ceiling) of the hall, meant that living and sleeping could be separated entirely. In farmhouses all the upstairs rooms became bedrooms or store rooms, indifferently known as 'chambers' in the past. In the surviving seventeenth-century inventories they are described as the 'chamber over the hall', the 'chamber over the parlour', the 'chamber over the kitchen' and so on. Often bed chambers were also used for storage, in particular the chamber over the kitchen. Samuel Taply of Teignmouth kept pease and butter and dried fish in this room in 1642, and here two of his men slept on 'douse' beds, mattress covers filled with chaff. This particular room seems to have often been the workmen's sleeping quarters and there is some evidence to show that it occasionally had an outside staircase. Thomas Blampin of Gittisham stored farm tools, a cheesewring and cheese vats in his 'men's room' in 1622, and there is a reference to a 'boys' chamber' in John Letheren's house in Winkleigh in 1646. John Warren of Talaton kept barley in his 'sealed chamber' in 1693, while Elizabeth Hellings, a rich Culmstock clothier, kept bales of cloth in the parlour chamber, the hall chamber, the hall and the parlour, as well as 115 scald-milk cheeses in the milkhouse chamber. There was still space for two beds in this room, however, and Edward Gould of Staverton had four bedsteads and 'four beds with coverlets blankets and bolsters for worke men' in his kitchen chamber. Farm boys slept over the cattle at least as late as the 1880s. Ernest Bevin, later Minister of Labour and Foreign Secretary, was consigned to this sort of sleeping quarters on Beers farm, near Copplestone, during his time on the farm.

The hall chamber seems to have been the best bedroom. Occasionally, it was elaborately furnished and in this room the silver and pewter was sometimes stored, perhaps for safety's sake. John Westlake of Topsham kept four silver bowls and ten silver spoons worth £10. 10s. in his hall chamber, and Nicholas Spicer kept 'a bowl of silver and a dozen of silver spoons and a carrick cup tipped with silver' in the same room; Grace Cooper of Cove kept all her pewter upstairs and George Good of St Thomas kept some fifty pieces of pewter in his bed chamber.

The parlour, once perhaps the solar, was also, curiously, used as a bedroom. Edward Gould had a bedstead with a green canopy and curtains in his parlour, and Alice Lee of Heavitree had a bed in hers, along with a table and benches and a couple of chests. John Letheren of Winkleigh, much poorer than either of the above, had a carpet and bed in his parlour too. Perhaps this downstairs room was used as a guest room.

All the upstairs chambers were originally inter-connecting, one room leading to the next from one staircase, with all the lack of privacy that that implied. The Revd Sabine Baring-Gould could remember how at Upcott in Broadwood Kelly, a gentleman's house, the maidservants who slept in the end room of one side of the house went to bed first, followed by the daughters of the house who slept in the next rooms. Then followed the menservants who lived in the end room at the other end, and so on until last of all the master and mistress, who slept in the master bedroom at the stair head, went to bed. What he does not explain is what happened in the morning. The desire for privacy in the end led to the creation of a landing at the head of the staircase. From the landing there were doors to the nearest rooms and a passage led generally along the back wall of the house to the other bedrooms. These passage ways were often very narrow and low since they had to be fitted in beneath the crucks where they existed, and built so that not too much front room space was lost. This development of the landing probably dates from the late seventeenth century, but there were certainly farmhouses still with interconnecting bedrooms in the next century. An enquiry into the housing and treatment of boy and girl farm apprentices in 1840 made this clear. Apprentices slept three to a bed and five or six to a room at that time and the girls had to go through the boys' rooms to get to their own. They sometimes shared the farmer's sons' and daughters' rooms. Farmhouses were scarcely big enough to house all the 'family'. A farm of 230 acres in Bridford in 1840 had a 'family' of twenty-one in the house.

Farm servants and the poor generally slept on 'douse' beds. Douse was the name for the waste that came out of the end of the threshing machine or was left after thrashing with a flail, once the corn and the straw had been separated. It is not quite chaff, though near enough, and consists of broken straws, husk and barley awns, and all the dusty material attached to straw. The material was stuffed into a canvas sack and this was a douse bed. William Harrison described servants sleeping conditions in these words: 'If they had any sheet above them it were well, for seldom had they any under their bodies to keep them from the pricking straw that ran often through the canvas of the pallet and rased their hardened hides.' The better-off slept on feather beds and it is the bed, what we would call the mattress, that is valued in the inventories. There were also flock beds and down beds. A bed with its bedstead and hangings was 'a bed performed'. The bedsteads could be low truckle beds, perhaps on casters, and 'tester' (four poster) or 'half tester' beds with full or half canopies and curtains. There were also occasionally 'fild' or field beds which seems to have been a bed with curtains suspended from a single point overhead to form a canopy like a tent. The night air was thought to be dangerous, so windows were kept closed and curtains around the bed were drawn to keep it out and also, of course, to provide some privacy where there was more than one bed to the room. Sewn into the hangings of the bed was a pocket for a pocket watch, once they became available. Beneath the bed was a chamber pot of tin or pewter or brass.

For lighting there was a tinder box and a home-made tallow candle in a cloam or tin candlestick. Getting a light from a tinder box, striking a spark to ignite the dry tinder, was often a lengthy and tedious business. Rush lights were also commonly used; a strip of rush was soaked and covered in tallow or grease and pinched into a rush light-holder like a pair of tweezers on a stand. Traditionally, rushes for this purpose were picked in the meadows by the village girls in May. Both these and candlesticks were sometimes made with sharp lateral spikes so that they could be pushed and fixed into a cob wall. Oil lamps using train oil, (whale oil), date from the first quarter of the nineteenth century and kerosene (paraffin) lamps from the last. Glass was initially too expensive for an easily breakable lantern, so thin strips of cows' horn were used with a candle inside to shed a feeble light. Folk went to bed and rose with the sun. At night, outside the big towns, the countryside must have been almost totally dark, 'black as the Earl of Hell's boots', on moonless nights with only the faintest glimmer of light from a candle in a farm kitchen, quite invisible from a distance, to greet the benighted traveller. Few probably travelled at night at all and most probably echoed Jorrock's dictum 'Where I dines I sleeps'. The faint candlelight from the window of a cottage in the dark of the forest or moor beckoning on the unwary traveller, is an archetypal image beloved of folk tales.

Newly created upper rooms had to have windows inserted and this was sometimes done in smaller houses by building 'chicket' or dormer windows protruding from the roof. In larger houses there was generally room to fit in a window in the front wall. But if the old hall had had windows to roof level then these had to be divided to accommodate the new floor. Eventually, as the standard of living rose, fireplaces would be inserted in the bedrooms, normally fitted with another flue into an existing chimney. Heated rooms upstairs were a sign of some prosperity, requiring servants to lay and clear the fire. Both John Warren of Talaton and Alice Newall of Uplyme had firedogs and tongs upstairs in their parlour chamber and hall chamber. The cast-iron bedroom grate is a nineteenth-century creation and most upstairs fireplaces must have been small-scale open fires with a thick hearth stone. One such survives at Poltimore farm in Farway. Alice Newall's inventory dates from 1593, but there is not much other evidence that upper rooms were commonly heated until a good deal later, except in town houses or much larger houses. The Yeos of Huish had a house with forty-one rooms, and only five of the upstairs chambers had fireplaces with tongs, bellows and irons and firepans. The Yeos were wealthy gentry; their house was perhaps not unusual for their class. Sir Richard Hawkins' great house at Pool in Slapton, long demolished, had no less than eighteen chimneys in the seventeenth century, some of which must have heated upper rooms.

The same century probably saw the introduction in the better farmhouses of the 'garderobe'. This was the medieval euphemism for the present euphemism, the 'loo' or 'toilet'. The vernacular word was the 'jakes', matched neatly by the American 'john'. (At no time have folk been prepared to call the 'WC', the 'toilet', the 'little room' or the Naval 'heads' what it is, the shithouse.) Garderobes were ordinary features in great houses in medieval times. They consisted of a shaft from first-floor level to ground level, built into or onto the back wall of the house. Sometimes there was no shaft, merely a protruding structure at first floor level that contained inside the appropriate seat and a hole below. It was doubtless an apprentice's or labourer's job to clean out and clear away the resulting accumulation. This was not wasted; farmers near a town commonly collected 'night-soil', another euphemism, to spread on the land. Fields near farmhouses sometimes bear the name 'Shiten Park', later bowdlerized to Sheep Park or something similar. Thomas Tusser advised that the cleaning of the privies should be done at night: 'let night be appointed such baggage to hide', and the result buried in the garden where it 'shall make very many things better to grow'. In Devon, apparently, the produce of the farmhouse was often mixed with wood ash in a purpose-built ash house in the farmyard, and spread on the meadowland. There were continuous supplies of ash from the wood fires kept constantly burning in the kitchen. Providing a jakes upstairs did away with the cold and nasty journey at night to the 'offices', as William Harrison calls it, a similar place across the farmyard. This upstairs 'jakes' was another sign of some wealth and sophistication. The normal arrangement, outside, was a shed over a large hole in the ground with seat or seats above, as it remained well into this century. It was not unknown for these jakes to be built over a stream, as was often done in towns. Such an arrangement was in use in a far from unsophisticated village in east Devon until very recently. An upstairs jakes still involved lighting a candle or stumbling about in the dark. To avoid this, the common-or-garden chamber pot (the pot for the chamber) was an early introduction. John Elliston, Vicar of Whitchurch, had 'two old chamber pots worth 14d.' in 1622. More sophisticated still was the 'jake stool or close stool', a portable chair suitably fitted up. This occurs in a number of inventories; there were two of them in Joane Sparke's hall chamber, and one in the chamber over the kitchen in John Vicary's house in Farway. Also mentioned are bedpans, although some of these were probably warming pans. In cloth making towns and villages urine was often collected by cart early in the morning for use in treating cloth. Celia Fiennes, writing in 1698, explained how rolls of serge were used to clean a room and then soaked in urine before soaping and fulling. Nothing was wasted.

There were other specialized rooms in the developed farmhouses. There are frequent references in the inventories to the wool chamber, the dairy or the milkhouse, and occasionally to the cockloft and the spence. The first of these was often apparently the room over the porch. Wool chamber implies an upstairs room and fleeces had to be kept dry and perhaps out of the way as they smelt, though not unpleasantly. The room over the porch would be airy and could be shut off and there is some evidence that this was how it was used. The dairy, or more commonly the milkhouse, must have been an early addition to the farmhouse once cheese and butter and cream making became important. Such activities were not possible in a hot and smoky kitchen or hall. The milkhouse was often at the back of the house out of the sun and latterly had a cold slate floor and slate shelves for standing the cream or milk, and hooks in the ceiling for 'roofmeat', as it was called, salted beef or mutton or pork. Almost every farm made cream or butter or cheese, frequently all three, and a cool dairy was essential for these activities.

The cockloft was the space between the ceiling of an upper room and the actual roof. It appears most commonly in tall, narrow town houses, but Alice Newall of Uplyme had one in her house in 1593, housing a chest and bench and a couple of saddles, and Edward Gould of Staverton kept a child's chair, a pig's skin, a coffer and a spinning wheel in his in 1628. It was perhaps an attic for cast offs, things no longer in use. Presumably it acquired its name from its situation, where once, in less sophisticated days, the cock perched at night, 'the pullen o'er the beam'. The spence made use of a bit of space newly created by the building of a staircase. It was traditionally the cupboard or small room under the stairs and was used for storage. Philip Buckingham of Upton Hellions had a spence and 'a little spence' in which he kept a 'still', a cupboard and a desk and a couple of curtain rods, perhaps, as with the cockloft, out of the way. 'Spence' is still occasionally used in farmhouses to-day. It was presumably, originally, a store room whence supplies were 'dispenced'.

Some houses had a number of these specialist rooms. Perhaps rather large, but not untypical of a yeoman's farmhouse in the seventeenth century, was that of John Warren of Talaton. He died in 1693 and his goods and chattels were valued at £158. 4s. His house consisted of, downstairs: a parlour, a kitchen, a hall, (all with fireplaces), a servants' hall, and an inner dairy and an outer dairy full of cheese-making equipment and barrels. Upstairs were a corn chamber and a stable chamber, used for storing cheeses and wheat and oats and wool. These may have been in an outhouse but were clearly on an upper floor. There were also a hall chamber, a middle chamber, a broad chamber, a porch chamber, a sealed chamber, and a parlour chamber that had a fireplace. All of these were bedrooms, though barley was stored in the sealed chamber as well as the bed. There were also a kitchen chamber and a malt chamber used for storing husbandry tools and for brewing, and a study chamber which housed only twenty-one pewter dishes. There is, curiously, no mention of a study below the study chamber and this is almost the only reference in the inventories to a servants' hall as such. Unlike many other yeomen, John Warren did not keep a bed in his parlour. There were, then, probably seventeen rooms in his house with seven beds in his six bed chambers. He was not by the standard of the inventories that survive a rich farmer: he had eleven cattle, thirty sheep, three horses and five pigs worth £58; and his dead stock, hay and corn and implements were worth £45. His household goods, which included a clock, were worth nearly £70. He seems to have had some property, furniture, beds and chests and cider press in Sidmouth, all of which were included in his valuation.

John Warren was a yeoman; Margery Rogers of Bondleigh was a widow, who was still carrying on her late husband's farm when she died. This was not uncommon; a widow often had the right under manorial custom, 'freebench' as it was called, to her husband's holding on his death and there was often no other means of livelihood available to her. Perhaps Christopher Rogers, who put his mark to her inventory by way of signature, was her son who actually worked the holding. She had a house of four rooms, a hall, a hall chamber, a parlour and parlour chamber, and the value of all her goods and chattels was £58. 17s. She had six cattle, twenty sheep, seven pigs and poultry worth £22, no horses but a yoke of ploughing oxen, dead stock, hay and corn and implements worth £13, and her household goods made up the rest (£23); there were five beds in her house and she had some books, rather surprisingly, and twenty-eight pewter dishes. She should be described, if such a word is possible, as a 'husbandwoman'.

Floors, walls and ceilings

Traditional farmhouse kitchens have blue slate slabs for a floor. These are first and foremost easy to keep clean and well-swept, as they shed no dust. They acquire with time a kind of polish or patina and they look very well even when they are cracked. In some houses they sweat or 'heave' as the relative humidity of the air changes and an observant farmer could use this phenomenon to forecast or recognize changes in the weather. They were laid over the bare earth if there were no sort of floor underneath and in a cold kitchen can by very cold. But kitchens were and are warm spots and a slate floor, though not a surface for bare feet, takes on the warmth of the room. They were commonly used in halls and entries and can vary from very finely and carefully laid perfect slabs to the roughest of uneven irregular blocks. Some have attractive fine lines of quartz running through them and in east Devon a slate was used that takes on the curious yellowish tinge. They were probably always rather expensive, since slate was not easily obtainable in all parts of the South West. Harberton, near Totnes, and Delabole, in North Cornwall, produced fine blue slates but the source of the east Devon slates is not known.

The most common hard flooring in the past was lime ash. This is a product of the burning of lime. Limestone was burnt in lumps and came out of the kiln largely in the same form but another product was lime ash, which was in fact fine lime that had crumbled of the lumps. Limekilns were started by burning wood or culm with the stone, but once the limestone had got really hot combustion proceeded under its own heat and this produced the fine ash. This was laid straight on the earth of the floor and wetted. It then set somewhat in the manner of concrete. There is a tradition that it was wetted with blood to form a really hard floor but there is no good evidence of this. It was hard but inevitably it was dusty and needed a lot of sweeping. Lime ash floors probably became common when the use of lime as soil improver became customary in the seventeenth century. Before that time there had always been a need for lime mortar and lime for plaster work, but it does not seem likely that lime ash was available in quantity enough to floor every downstairs room until there was a lime kiln in almost every parish. Both lime ash and blue flag floors were probably covered and warmed by rush matting or rag rugs; carpets are mentioned in the inventories, but until more recent times it seems that these were used as table and bed coverings. Thomas Tusser has a list of herbs for 'strowing' on floors: basil and fennel and lavender and marjoram. Perhaps in his day (1573) these were for mixing with the traditional rushes on the earth floor. Poultry and cats and dogs and geese were not uncommon inhabitants of the kitchen, even in recent times.

Rather beautiful but necessarily uneven floors could be created out of cobbles or sets. These were probably useless for rooms but suitable for passage ways. They were created by laying pebbles, or popples as they were once called, in regular patterns on a lime ash base. This could be done very decoratively. Much the same could be done using local stone cut or broken into sets and inserted on end quite deeply into a lime ash base or outside into plain earth. Both pebbles and sets could be set very closely to form a hard wearable surface. Sets are still often seen in churchyard paths. The earliest floors in ordinary houses, however, were probably bare earth, traditionally covered with rushes or rudely covered with uneven slabs of stone. Upstairs, wood was inevitable, the earlier floors laid with uneven planking or 'planching' as it was known, straight from the saw-pit with little regard for true joins or regularity. Raised wooden floors downstairs lying on joists are probably nineteenth century. They were a great deal warmer to the foot, but unless ventilated, the joists tended to rot.

Walls and wall coverings

Frequently the 'entry' of the house, the cross passage, had a fine wooden screen on one side. This was mounted on a low plinth and fitted into the ceiling above, so it constituted a solid wall. In some houses, usually of better quality, there were screens on both sides of the passage. These screens are often beautifully and skilfully carpentered and joined, almost invariably morticed and tenoned and pegged, not nailed, with arched doorways and chamfered and stopped studs between the panels. These in turn were sometimes painted and coloured rather like the panels of a church screen. They were clearly expensive and were almost certainly designed to impress a visitor. It was 'conspicuous consumption' in fact, since there was no obvious reason why a plain stud and plaster, or stone or cob wall could not have been built in the same place. It is clear that at one time screens were designed to be movable to divide off the hall as needed and it was possibly easier to move them if they were in one well-carpentered piece. It is not a far step from that to something more elaborate to please the eye and often these screens are very elegant. Probably in the last century, many of these seventeenth-century masterpieces were boarded over and plastered and remain within a thin partition wall awaiting discovery.

The other walls of the hall were cob or stone. Cob was probably plastered by the well-off from an early date since otherwise it creates dust, but stone walls were often covered with painted cloths or hangings of some sort, perhaps for warmth's as much as appearance's sake. Joan Brownscombe, a fisherwoman of Dawlish, who died in 1590 had 'painted cloths' in her inventory; John Whitfield, a weaver of Landkey, had 'painted cloth at the hyedays price'; George Hocken of Totnes, a much richer man, had 'hangings of painted leather' in his house in 1602. A number of the bed chambers had hangings of some sort in the best bedrooms of Arras or tapestry or of 'saye' and of red or blue colour. There are not very many references to hangings in the the inventories, but curtains with a vallance were fairly common, some of them made from on apparently expensive material like 'green shadow' or 'with a silk fringe'. Sometimes walls were panelled or sealed and this sealing was clearly moveable as it forms part of an inventory, but this method of wall covering does not seem to have been common. Sealings of this kind with a bench fixed in front still survive in some old houses. Baring-Gould could remember how appallingly dark fully panelled rooms were in the days of candles and gave this a reason why this often elegant panelling was frequently painted white.

One sign of wealth was to have a plaster ceiling highly decorated and patterned with pendants and finials in the parlour or hall. This does not figure in the inventories as it was a fixture but the Abbot family of Fremington became specialists in this kind of work and their pattern books have survived from the seventeenth century. They travelled all over Devon to do their work which was highly specialized and doubtless expensive, and not within the reach of an ordinary farmer. There are, however, quite a number of not so large or imposing farm houses with plaster ceilings and a great many merchants were able to afford them in their town houses.

The more normal ceiling was that of the exposed beams of the first floor. These most frequently ran from the front to the back of the house but occasionally houses have ceilings with beams running from front to back and side to side and cunningly carpentered to marry together. These clearly were expensive and presumably designed for show since there does not seem to be any evidence that such ceilings were designed to carry an extra weight. Rooms upstairs were certainly used for storage as well as sleeping but there were few purpose-built upstairs granaries within the house. Beams were chamfered and stopped. That is, their corners were sawn or adzed off ('chamfered'), probably again for appearance's sake, until just before they actually entered the wall, where they were left rectangular. Where the rectangle of the beam, as it emerges from the wall, becomes the pentagon of the chamfer is the 'stop'. This carved feature could be elaborate or simple and lent itself to great variation in design. It thus becomes a good dating feature, since there seems to be an accepted chronological change in the design, early stops and late stops, the later ones far more elaborate than the earlier. Normally beams were stopped and chamfered in the better rooms. In outhouses and farm buildings they were left untouched. But good timber was always too dear to discard, so much can now be found where it was not originally used, and this can often be seen in door heads or beams with sockets cut into them, without any obvious function. Sometimes good chamfered beams occur in what can never have been anything but a farm building. Exposed beams are fashionable now but in Victorian times many such ceilings got totally covered in or the beams themselves encased in some way or plastered. The keys for the plaster, shallow cuts in the wood, are often visible. It seems to have been common to build another planked floor just over one that was worn out, rather than take up the old floor and lay a new one. This creates a double floor, a false floor, a paradise for mice, and sometimes a repository of long lost trifles. In the same way, the space between the ceiling beams could be boarded over ('underdrawn') and ceiled. In these spaces valuables and occasionally weapons or contraband were sometimes hidden, only accessible from the chamber above. From the beams of the kitchen, bacon and hams and occasionally spare Christmas puddings were hung out of the way of vermin. Here too the last sheaf of corn from the last harvest, the 'neck' as it was called, found a home for the year and bunches of herbs were hung and mistletoe at Christmas 'vor the bwoys to kiss the maidens under'.

The farm kitchen

This was the most important room in the house; here one part of the farm's work was done; here the family were fed and all their food was prepared and cooked; here everyone sat down together to eat and keep company (figs 13, 14). Here, almost certainly, all but the most distinguished guests were entertained. In the smaller houses the hall, once it had been ceiled over, often became the kitchen, and what would have been called in the old days, 'the entry' became eventually the hall, as it still is. Many old large houses had detached kitchens, but this seems to have been unusual in the rural South West, although common enough in towns. It was also not uncommon for the room below the cross passage to become the kitchen, and the hall to remain as the best living room with the parlour beyond. In earlier days all cooking had been done in the hall.

The farmer's wife, the housewife, presided over the kitchen. Not so long ago it was traditional for a farmer to give his wife no housekeeping money at all. She was expected to keep all the household going, feed all the family and the farm servants, provide enormous threshing and harvest dinners, find or make clothes for the family, buy replacement cloam, china or crockery for the kitchen table, all from her own earnings. If there was any housekeeping money handed over from the sale of corn or cattle or wool, it was often done grudgingly. The test of a good wife was how far she could make her money go. One remark tells all. 'She makes a shilling go as far as the next woman', was the response of one farmer to a neighbour's praise of his wife's miraculous thrift and efficiency. In fact this apparent meanness was not so absurd as it seems today. Bacon, eggs and

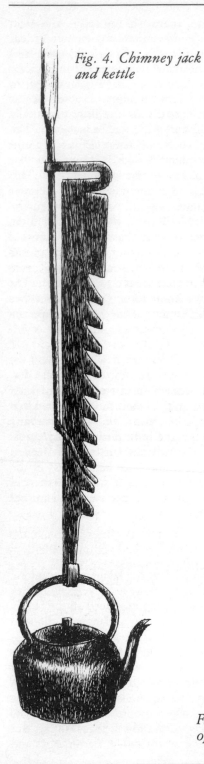

Fig. 4. Chimney jack
and kettle

Fig. 5. Hanging kettle on a brandis

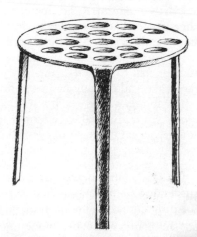

Fig. 6. Trivet: stand for cooking on an
open fire

poultry, cheese, butter, cream, honey, and vegetables were all very saleable products, and in the West Country there was always a good market for these. Feeding the townspeople was one role of the farm, but throughout the West Country there were other consumers: miners, fishermen, cloth workers, who all had to be fed and who formed an important part of the population. So every week or so a farmer's wife would set off to market, in a pony and trap if she were a latter-day yeoman's wife, or, in earlier times, she would ride side-saddle with a loaded packhorse on a rein behind her. If her man were merely a poor husbandman, she would have to trudge the five or six miles to market laden with maunds, or baskets, of her produce. How much she had to sell depended largely on her own industry and that of the farm servants she had to supervise.

Few farms were too small to have a farm servant or two. These were often parish apprentices, boys and girls, orphans or illegitimate 'hedge' children, for whom the parish was responsible. They provided cheap labour but they were not by any means always badly treated, and they sat at the bottom of the kitchen table with the farmer and formed part of his 'family' in its old sense. (For a fuller account of farm apprentices, see pp. 159–161, 'The Household') Servant girls would have done much of the work in the kitchen in the bigger farmhouses, but it was the housewife's business to supervise and organize, and in the smaller houses she doubtless did much of the work herself. This work centred of course around the hearth. In the old hall houses this was in the middle of the floor. William Harrison, lamented the passing of the old central open hearth with what he describes as a 'reredos' beside it (fig. 1). This must have been some kind of free-standing stone structure, against which the fire was built and to which perhaps spits and crooks and pots and pans could be attached or suspended. Such an object does not seem to appear in any of the few early inventories, under that name or any other, in the South West, but its use seems as likely here as in Harrison's Essex.

Harrison regretted the changed position of the hearth from the centre of the floor to a chimney, because he thought the smoke was good for the house and for its inhabitants. In the past,

> each one made his fire against a reredos in the hall where he dined and dressed his meat. Now have we many chimnies and yet our tenderlings complain of rheums and catarh...then had we none but reredoses and our heads did never ache. For as the smoke in those days was supposed to be a sufficient hard[en]ing for the timber of the house so it was reputed a far better medicine to keep the goodman and his family from the quacke or pose, wherewith as then very few were acquainted.

On this central hearth, around a wood fire, spits or 'broches' could be suspended from free-standing bearers or brackets, with all kinds of fittings for different sizes and kinds of meat. These spits in early times must have been turned by hand, not without some risk of scorching. Children, traditionally, in great households were given this job. The spit was set slightly away from the centre of the fire since beneath it was an iron pan, a 'dripping' pan, to catch the fat. All sorts of other cooking pots were devised

Fig. 7. Baking kettle used as an oven in an open fire, piled with hot peat, 'vags' or ash. It could also be used upright.

Fig. 8. Wooden trencher with place for salt

Fig. 9. Brass skillet

Fig. 10. Trivet

to enable food to be cooked without the cook getting burnt (figs. 4, 5, 7, 9, 10), and there was a 'savingire', which seems to have been some kind of fire shield. Posnets, later called skillets, were three-legged saucepans often made of brass or bell metal with a handle, that could be pushed into the ashes and a 'brandis' was a trivet, a three-legged support for a pot in the middle of the fire. Almost invariably, therefore, three-cornered fields are called Brandis Park; and Brandis Cross or Brandis Corner is where three roads meet. A brandis might be round with three legs, as well as three-cornered, as the old riddle reveals.

> So round as a hoop so black as a crow
> Three legs and a thumping hole.

Frying pans and griddles appear in many inventories and seem to be just like present versions, except that the griddle was a flat plate fixed to an iron bow, suspended over the fire from a crook. The gridiron, on the other hand, was a circular barbecue grill with a long handle. The bars of this were quite wide and concave in section, so that fat could be caught within the hollow. Often as part of the handle there was a sizeable bowl into which all the fat could run from the bars. Toasters were made that could be pushed into the fire with a sort of rack for the bread that could be swivelled round to allow both sides to be toasted (fig. 17). Many kitchens had caldrons, skimmers, 'searches', which were fine strainers, chafing dishes, 'perypans' and kettles, fleshpikes or pikes for handling hot meat, catherines – a kind of cauldron – and goosepans for fat, all of them open-fire gear. One nineteenth-century feature was a pipe rack. This was an open cylinder of iron in which used, dirty clay pipes could be stacked, for roasting clean of their dottle and nicotine on the fire.

'Crocks' are often mentioned in the inventories, and these appear not to be of pottery but of quite valuable brass or bell metal, which was easier perhaps to clean or polish than the fairly rough cast or wrought iron. They must originally have been clay vessels replaced by more durable brass. They were large boiling or stewing bowls with either a single handle to hang from a crook, or two for use on a brandis.

Kettles in Devon were often 'baking kettles' for use on an open fire, not for boiling water (fig. 7). They were in two pieces: a flat fairly thick iron plate, on which an iron bowl could be inverted. This bowl had three small feet so that it could be used upright as well. Bread dough or meat could be placed on the flat plate covered with the bowl and pushed into the fire to be then covered over with the burning ashes or 'vags' (turves). The food would cook as if in an oven. Hot meals could be left to cook in this way and these kettles were in use, on Dartmoor at least, well into this century.

Cooking on an open fire in a chimney was probably not much different to cooking against a reredos. Absolutely essential, in both fires probably, were andirons, or andogs, or firedogs, which occur in almost every inventory. These were designed to keep the burning logs from falling out and also to raise the fire a few inches from the level of the hearth to give a very necessary draught. Ash could be raked out below the andogs and stored in an ash house. Andirons or andogs had fore feet and hind feet and a back and a sort of round knob-like head, sometimes made of brass. They too were described in a riddle

Head like an apple, neck like a swan,
Back like a long dog and three legs to stand on.

With the chimney fire some elaboration of cooking arrangements was possible. Firstly a baking oven came into use, built into the chimney wall, with its own flue leading into the main chimney. In this bread and perhaps meat was baked. The oven was heated by setting fire to a faggot of brushwood inside and allowing all the wood to be burnt to ash. By that time the oven was very hot, and the ash was raked away as need be, the bread set out inside using a long oven peal, and the door replaced and sealed with clay. Baking ovens are common in old West Country houses, often made of brick. Eventually, purpose-built cloam (clay) 'Barnstaple ovens' were made in some numbers in potteries at Barnstaple and Truro and inserted into chimneys. There were problems with these; once the clay door cracked it was apparently almost impossible to make a satisfactory new one that fitted tightly enough, so iron doors had to be used. By the nineteenth century the open fire and the wall oven began to be replaced by the cast iron range, which was able, using one comparatively small coal fire, to boil, bake, fry and roast. Two firms in Devon made these in particular, Bodleys of Exeter and Lidstones of Kingsbridge. The Bodley stove was much loved by Devon housewives, and was clearly of great use where coal was cheap, that is not too far from the coast. Elsewhere, the open fire and the clay oven continued well into this century. Although 'cowls' (covers) for the fire are sometimes mentioned in inventories, cooking on these fires invariably meant, for the housewife, singed and scorched knuckles and fingers, and a red face.

For the open fire a ready and easy supply of faggots and cord wood in never-ending supplies was vital. Farmers didn't have to go far for firewood; every newly laid hedge produced its quota. Hence the pyramids and piles of hedgewood close to the farmhouse door in the old days; essential to keep the fire alight continuously throughout the year. A really cold, unrevivable fire was a disaster for the housewife, and involved fussing about with bellows – the 'bellises' of the inventories – , a tinder box, and a 'blast of vuzz' – an armful of furze. Phosphorus matches only became easily available about a hundred years ago. If the fire had died for lack of wood there was surely trouble for someone.

The hearth was the real focus and centre of the house (figs. 12, 13). Here the outside, 'outdel', workers gathered at meal times for food and warmth, and here in the evening the master of the house, 'the maister' would sit, smoking his clay churchwarden pipe, and drinking rough cider or a nip of still liquor, playing crib or telling tales. The fireplace was surmounted by a clavel beam of granite or oak, often of a huge size since it had to support some of the weight of the chimney. This could be inscribed with dates and initials; in gentry houses there was sometimes a royal coat of arms above. Within the chimney there were often stone seats, or wooden stools for favoured visitors or family, the inglenooks. Above the clavel beam was the 'clavy tack' or mantelpiece, and on this would be tobacco jars and tinder boxes and perhaps an hour glass in the old days. Up the chimney beyond the crooks, farmers sometimes hung their hams to smoke and sometimes placed a small magic image on a ledge to keep the witches away. Human intruders might be deterred by sharp upward pointing spikes fixed into the chimney. Occasionally, built into the chimney, out of sight and inaccessible, except when the fire was cold, was a recess or cupboard for cheap smuggled spirits.

Possibly some element of sociability was lost when the range replaced the open fire. It was probably less attractive and less warm to sit in front of a range, though it might be less draughty. Ranges came to be associated with kitchens, whereas open fires were very much part of the old, all-purpose hall. 'Dining' and 'dressing of the meat' were eventually done in quite separate rooms.

Other elaborations were possible with an open cooking fire in a chimney. Firstly, the chimney was fitted with iron bars from wall to wall from which adjustable chimney crooks could be hung. These appear in almost every inventory. On these cauldrons and griddles and the more conventional type of kettle were suspended (fig. 4), their height determined by the ratchet arrangement on the crook. The kettle often had a vertical pivot by which it could be tipped without taking off the fire. 'Crane irons', bolted to the side or back of the chimney, enabled kettles or saucepans to be swung sideways at will. All these devices gave some control over the degree of heat to be applied. This was important, as some operations, like scalding cream, needed careful and delicate adjustment so that the milk should not boil. Originally all the hot water needed in the house was boiled in cauldrons or crocks suspended over the fire. In later times and bigger houses there was a copper cauldron fitted into a brick structure in the back kitchen with its own small chimney and a flue beneath, into which furze faggots were thrust to make a quick hot fire. This was the 'copper', and the very best fuel for this was a faggot of 'black sticks' furze that had been singed before cutting to remove the prickles. In this copper the water was boiled for the weekly wash for the whole household.

Roasting spits were also improved. The most sophisticated device for turning a spit was a large iron fan suspended horizontally in the chimney which was turned by the rush of hot air up the chimney and was geared to the spit. There were, also, probably by the end of the seventeenth century, weight driven clockwork spits and, later, spring-driven machinery that could be wound up. A vertical spring-driven spit, hung in front of the fire with an iron guard to reflect the heat, also came into use. In St Briavel's Castle (Gwent), above the hearth, is a 'dog wheel', inside which a small dog could be induced to walk continuously to keep the spit moving. The inducement, so it is said, was a sprinkling of hot cinders inside the wheel! These were apparently once used in farmhouses in Devon, built into small recesses, now often cupboards, beside the fireplace. All this gear made the housewife's work easier, and apart from the cast iron cooking stove, much of it was within the capacity of a good local blacksmith.

Kitchen furnishings

The central feature of a kitchen was a 'table board' and 'forms', the table and benches. The table was often on trestles so it could be taken down to store against the wall. In the middle of this, at meal times, stood the 'salt', often an object of some value and status, valued separately in inventories and bequeathed separately in wills; it was probably in some way a symbol of hospitality. Family and honoured guests sat above the salt, working men and servants below it. Sometimes the table board was replaced by a 'side board'. This was not initially a place for crockery or pewter, but a table against the wall to sit at and eat from. Benches also were sometimes built into the wall. Forms were like old-fashioned school benches the length of the table. Occasionally there were stools, 'joint stools' (made by a joiner) or chairs; these could be cane, reed, wicker or leather-covered or 'low' chairs. But there are no references to upholstered armchairs. These and the sofa must be of nineteenth-century date, and then were for the parlour only. Folk at leisure sat on settles which appear first in some numbers in the seventeenth century. Nicholas Smith, a gentleman of Totnes, had a 'bank to sit by the fire' in 1558. Settles, sealed or panelled down to floor level, did give a draught-proof seat on which to roast in front of the fire, probably the only really warm place in the house other than inside a bed (fig. 11). They were firstly just upright seats, but later the bacon settle became fairly usual with cupboards incorporated in the back to store bacon away from dogs or cats. The most usual place for salted smoked meat, however, was the ceiling, either hung from hooks or on a suspended bacon rack.

There was good deal of other kitchen furniture. One of the most common in the seventeenth century was the amory or aumbrie (French: *armoire*), which was some kind of cupboard. This word has been completely lost. Another sort of cupboard quite common in the seventeenth century, was the 'press'; it had shelves mainly for clothes or linen. Press is still the normal Irish word for a cupboard. Chests and coffers were also common, with locks and keys. Spruce (Prussian) and danske (Danzig) chests were highly valued and were clearly imported from the Baltic. 'Cup boards' were common, but like the side board they had a different use from that of today, as they were merely boards for cups, probably screwed to a wall. 'Shelf boards' were the same, and probably moveable. A standing cupboard was a proper piece of furniture not attached to a wall, and these appear fairly late and rarely in the inventories. There are few references to drawers, or chests of drawers, and equally few to dressers. All these were, however, common farmhouse furniture in the nineteenth century, and in the kitchen there was often a corner cupboard and a cupboard built into the thickness of the cob wall close to the fire for salt and tea and other household goods. Often above the fire, on the 'clavy tack', was a wooden salt box to keep the salt dry. A 'hutch' is often mentioned in inventories and this was still known in farmhouse kitchens fifty years ago. It was a small open-fronted cupboard for loose flour or other cooking materials, easily accessible to the cook's hand. Dressers are not common in the inventories but became an almost universal feature by the nineteenth century, with three or four drawers

Fig. 11. A 'bacon' settle: a draught-proof seat and storage for sides of bacon.

Fig. 12. Traditional Devon kitchen fireplace, showing cooking apparatus and characteristic hearth furniture.

Fig. 13. View of the traditional Devon kitchen, looking towards the hearth

Fig. 14. *The traditional kitchen, looking the other way towards the cross passage*

or cupboards below and four or more shelves above to house the treen trenchers, the pewter or cloam plates and saucers and, eventually, expensive 'cheyney' (china).

In medieval times most folk ate off wooden 'treen' trenchers, either round wooden plates at least half an inch thick, or square with a scooped out circular hollow in the middle and a small similar hollow for salt (fig. 8). At one time these hollows were actually scooped out in the table top itself. These trenchers were of course unbreakable, easy to clean and cheap, and were for their purpose, doubtless, better than earthenware or cloam which must have been in use at the same time. By the sixteenth century pewter was coming into use and the wooden trencher was for the servants or labourers only. By the seventeenth century even quite poor households boasted a few pewter dishes or vessels. Richard Reynolds of Moretonhampstead, who died in 1645 with goods valued at £16, had eighteen pewter dishes worth £1. 10s. among his kitchen gear. Pewter was, in fact, always less common than brass, which was, however, confined to much larger cooking pots and crocks. There were other utensils of tin and latten, leather and, rarely, of bell metal (fig. 18). Pewter, if polished is beautiful, and old silver pewter can hardly be distinguished in appearance from silver itself, so it was a prized possession. 'Cloam' was earthenware, and was by the end of the seventeenth century the cheapest form of kitchenware. Most towns probably had a potter, just as the larger towns in Devon all had a pewterer. Fair Day was the traditional time to buy up a year's supply of cloam and most big villages or towns had a fair, generally in summer time.

The inventories of personal goods end too soon to allow 'china', more properly porcelain, to figure very much. However, some gentry had 'china' in the seventeenth century, but this must have been imported, since English porcelain manufacture did not begin until the eighteenth.

It is worth looking at the household goods of Mistress Anne Parnacott of Petrockstow, way up in north-west Devon, the widow of a tolerably wealthy yeoman. She died worth £378 in 1635. Her farm goods were worth £223 and she had a lease on some land in Peter's Marland valued at £60. All the rest of her belongings were clothing, furniture and kitchen gear. She had, in her farmhouse, a cup with a cover of gilt, one silver salt worth £3. 3s., a dozen and a half of silver spoons, seven featherbeds with rugs, coverlets and blankets, a spruce chest and three other chests and coffers, three pairs of sheets, four table cloths, two dozen table napkins, one tin salt, one tin cup, two tin candlesticks and three of brass, six brazen pots, nine brass pans, one cauldron, one skillet, one pestle and mortar, one chafing dish, four dripping pans, three crane irons, three pot crooks one grid iron, one toaster and wooden vessels – most of these in the kitchen. She also had, probably in the hall, a musket, two long table boards, a square form and chair, one carpet and four cushions, one cupboard, one grater and Venice glass jugs and glasses, her clothes, and money in her purse. Finally, in store she had beef and bacon, tallow, mort (lard) and butter.

Fig. 15. Brass pestle and mortar

Fig. 16. Rack for clay pipes. It could be suspended over a fire to burn out the dottle from the pipes.

Fig. 17. Two different toasters for the open fire

The dairy or milkhouse

It is a rare sight to see the farmer himself with his clouted shoon and his fustian coat, ribbed blue and black stockings, breeches of corduroy, to see him arousing his household at 5 o'clock and his wife hurrying the servant wenches as they call them from their beds. His wife is ready to take a turn at the churn or to turn up her gown sleeves and kneeling down on a straw cushion to press the sweet curd to the bottom of the cheese pan.

William Howitt Rural Life in England

One of the most important rooms in the farmhouse was the dairy or milkhouse. Almost all farms made butter and cream and cheese for their own use and for a great many, regular sales of 'whitsul' created a good cash income.

> Good housewife in dairy that needs not to be told
> Deserveth her fee to be paid her in gold.

So the farmer's wife and her maid spent a lot of time in the dairy. This was often a cool room with fly-proof windows for a draught and good doors to keep cats and dogs out. On the roof were hooks for hams and against the wall were racks for cheeses; somewhere for certain was a mouse trap. Not far away, in the kitchen or in an outhouse with a copper, was a supply of hot water. Trial and error would have dictated that the brazen crocks and wooden pails of the dairy should be kept clean.

Until this century few farmers, except around the towns, sold fresh milk in any quantity. On the other hand, almost every farmer kept some cattle and bred from them. Cattle, if left to themselves, will naturally drop their calves in the spring to coincide with the flush of grass at that time and almost invariably on good grass they will produce far more milk than their calf needs. A calf rarely sucks his dam dry at a meal, it takes two or more calves at least to do that, and if a cow is milked before a calf has sucked, there is normally enough for the calf as well. Regular, complete hand milking also stimulates the cow to continue to produce milk. So the farmer was faced with the problem, when his cows had all calved, of what to do with the surplus milk. This was so in the past just as it is today, and in the past there was very little sale for liquid milk. So the milk had to be turned into something sellable: this was of course butter and cheese and, to some lesser extent, cream. On most farms there was no escaping this spring and summer task. From April to November ('From April beginning till Andrew[1] be past, So long with good housewife her dairy doth last.') the cows had to be milked twice a day and the milk either scalded to make cream and scalded milk or churned to make butter and skim milk, or treated with rennet from a cow's stomach to make cheese and whey. Some of the milk went to the calf but all the rest had to be treated in some way every day if it was not to be wasted. Cows went pretty well dry in winter until two or three months before calving again, so there was probably always

---

[1] St Andrew's day, 30 November

Fig. 18. Leather drinking vessels or 'blackjacks'

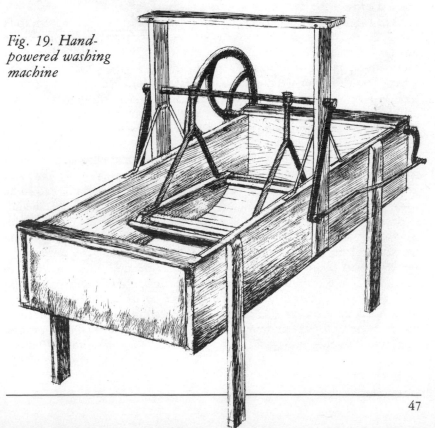

Fig. 19. Hand-powered washing machine

Fig. 20. A free-standing 'oven' or stove with copper pan for 'raising' cream. Inside is a grill for the burning charcoal.

Fig. 21. Patterns, for walking through muddy farmyards

Fig. 22. Brass 'crocks' used in cream making

a cow or two to milk; but the bulk of this work was summer work and it was entrusted normally to the farmer's wife and the dairymaid if there was one. The men sometimes did the milking, but cheese and butter and cream were women's business.

Cream and butter

The first task for the farmer's wife or the dairy maid was to separate the cream from the milk in some way. This could be done either by using a churn or, in the South West, by scalding. Once separated, the cream could be sold or turned into butter and the skim or scalded milk could be made into cheese. The whey from cheese-making would go to the pigs.

The making of scalded or 'clotted' cream seems to have been confined in the past to the South West. The process of making this cream demands some care and attention. The new milk is first stood in large cream pans – perhaps the brass or earthenware 'crocks' of the inventories – overnight so that the cream may rise. It is then scalded, brought to a temperature not very far off the boil. But the milk must not boil; if it does, it is useless for making cream, so it must be watched. Traditionally, the right temperature was reached when the outline of the bottom of the pan could be seen on the surface of the heating milk or when tiny bubbles started to appear on the surface. When this happens the pan is taken off the heat and stood once again on the cold slate shelves of the dairy until it is cold. By then it will have formed a delectable yellow crust and this is skimmed off with a 'scummer', as the inventories have it. What is left is scalded milk and this can be turned into scald-milk cheeses or drunk. The clotted or 'clouted' cream can be eaten instead of butter on bread or used for cooking instead of butter, added in a dollop to a dish of vegetables or potatoes, eaten with stewed fruit, or pilchards, or on a cutround, split or tuffcake (never, in the past, on a scone) with strawberry jam. In the past, West Country people thought it went best of all with junket or with 'pastry of different sorts, which is usually served up with clouts of cream'.

Alternatively, the scalded cream could be stirred until it turned to butter direct and it was probably easier to make butter out of scalded milk than out of raw milk. Raw milk sometimes takes time to separate in a butter churn. The separation is very slow in some weather conditions, and requires considerable effort. Scalding, however, separates the cream from the milk easily and just requires heat, and some say the separation is more complete. Churns are not mentioned among the household goods in any of the inventories that survive from the past and the 'daya' or dairymaid, employed by the monks of Tavistock in the fifteenth century to make butter and cheese, had no churn either. It is clear that until the end of the eighteenth century butter was always made from scalded cream in the South West.

Heat for the scalding was provided either on the ordinary open fire or on a special slow-burning, purpose-built cream oven, which could be free-standing or built-in. On the open fire the milk was suspended from the chimney crook over a slow fire and had to be carefully watched. The chimney was sooty and the fire was smoky and these two combined to give the cream, and the butter made from it, a smoky taste much appreciated by West Country folk but not liked by Londoners. It was also thought, up country, that butter made from scalded cream did not have the smooth consistency of raw cream butter.

By the turn of the eighteenth century east Devon in particular was sending large quantities of butter to London and other markets, and it was this market that caused the farmers' wives to change their methods and introduce the butter churn to make butter from raw milk. Marshall noted the beginning of 'raw milk dairies' and the Revd James Windsor of Uffculme wrote in 1810 that churns had only been introduced in the Culm Valley about 1770. This kind of butter was for export. Cream, of course, continued to be made in farmhouses in the old way because, as Marshall said, with seeming approval, the west of England farmers 'preferred the pleasures of the palate to the profits of the dairy'.

It may be that this market for less smoky butter sparked off the introduction of the 'cream oven', as it was called (fig. 20). Made from cloam with a flue for a draught at the lower end and a grating to hold charcoal near the top, it looked more like a stove. Marshall remarked on these, saying that they were used by the better farmers and gentry. On this stove the cream would heat slowly and controllably, and there was less chance of contamination by fumes and ash from the slowly burning charcoal than from an open fire. Some of these ovens had a hole half-way up big enough for the snout of a bellows. Built-in ovens occur mostly close to the fire but not in the fireplace, and were simply made of rubble masonry with a flue and a round hole at the top on which the cream crocks stood. Sometimes these ovens are double, for two pans. The fumes from the charcoal must have just escaped into the kitchen and were taken by the draught up the chimney. Free-standing stoves were probably made by the same businesses that made the cloam bread ovens.

It is not all clear why this way of raising cream seems to have been confined to the South West. Marshall thought that the origins of the process might lie at a time when farmers had only two or three cows at the most. The yield of these, if made into butter, would hardly be enough to sell in a market, so the problem arose as to how to store up this milk to make a sufficiently large quantity. He wrote, 'How could a more fortunate process have been struck out than that of securing the milk and the cream from their natural propensity of entering the different stages of fermentation, than the application of fire; which at once secures the milk from acidity and the cream from putrefaction'. He was quite right; scalding pasteurized the cream. When enough had been accumulated it could be made into butter and sold. Butter in the South West was always heavily salted, five or six times as much salt was used in the fifteenth century as would be used today. It is, of course, less work and perhaps more efficient to separate cream in this way. There may be other, not easily recognizable, reasons for scalding cream, to do with the damp warm climate of the South West, the acid soil, and the particular breeds of dairy cattle with fairly high butter fat and a yellow tinge to the milk. Centuries of trial and error perhaps culminated in this practical technique. It seems likely that the process is an ancient one, and it is possible that it was once common practice everywhere in the country, but survived only in the rather isolated South West. It has clearly been a regional speciality and regional delicacy for a very long time, though it can be made anywhere. One writer rudely suggested that if such cream, made elsewhere by up-country folk, does not have the authentic taste, it is because the cream pans are too clean! Farmers' wives often make clotted cream today by scalding a pan of mechanically separated cream, not the raw milk.

Celia Fiennes, who rode through Devon and Cornwall in 1698, was the first to describe clotted cream. She wrote that at St Austell:

> my Landlady brought me one of the West Country tarts, this was the first I met with, though I had asked for them in many places in Somerset and Devonshire; it's an apple pie with the custard all on the top, it's the most acceptable entertainment that could be made me; they scald their cream and milk in most parts of those counties and so it's a sort of clouted cream as we call it with a little sugar and so put on top of the apple pie.

Over a century earlier Edmund Spenser referred to 'clouted cream' in the *Shepherd's Calender*.

Cheese

The South West has no nationally known cheese like Cheddar, Cheshire, Wensleydale or Double Gloucester. These are all full-milk cheeses not made of scald or skim milk, and it may be that the scalding of milk made it impossible to produce really good cheese. Marshall noted how blue the skim milk was after scalding. Yet judging by the inventories of the past, every other farm had a cheese press, or a cheese wring as it was called. These survive in museums and were still being used on farms in this century. They ceased to be used only when it became easier and more profitable to sell raw milk, that is, just before the last war. Cheese, of course, preserves milk longest and best and was easily sellable during the winter months to provide a regular income for the farmer's wife. A cheese once pressed, coated with butter and encased in cheese cloth, will last for months in a cold place. If there is any deterioration it probably takes the form of the cheese going 'vinid', veined with green mould along a crack in the surface like Stilton or Dorset Blue Vinney. Eventually cheese mites take over these veins; they were thought by some to be the best thing about cheese, and were scraped out to be eaten first.

Possibly the bulk of the milk produced during the spring and summer months went into cheese-making. The dairymaid on Tavistock Abbey's Werrington estate made her first cheese on 23 April 1298 and continued to make roughly a cheese a day, Sundays included, until Michaelmas, 25 September. She made in all 160 cheeses that year, each cheese weighing half a stone, or 8 lb by Devonshire measure. (By this the dairy stone weighed 16 lb not 14 lb.) During that season she made therefore some

11 cwt of cheese, and only 4 st. of butter. Other years she made double that amount. At Werrington and the other Tavistock dairies, ewes were milked as well as cows and contributed more of the milk. There is no evidence of this practice in more recent times in the South West. At Hurdwick, near Tavistock, in the fifteenth century cows were expected to produce only 32 lb of cheese each and 4 lb of butter a year.

In 1646 Alice Lee had eighteen scald-milk cheeses in the chamber over the hall in her house at Heavitree.She had three cows and a heifer on her farm, and she owned a cheese wring. Salomon Westbeare of Culmstock had twenty-four cheeses and a cheese rack, but no wring and five cows in 1592, while Elizabeth Hellings, a rich clothier of Culmstock, died possessed of 115 cheeses in 1669 and ten head of cattle. Her cheeses and Westbeare's were worth 8d. and 3½d. each respectively, but Alice Lee's scald-milk cheeses were worth 5s. each. Clearly two quite different types or sizes of cheese are being valued. All three died towards the end of the cheese-making season when cheeses must have been in good supply. John Warren of Talaton in east Devon had what was perhaps a fairly typical set-up, with an inner and an outer dairy in 1693. In these he kept, among other things, eight brass pans, eight cheese vats, two cheese 'bords', one salting standard (measure), 'the victuals there in salt, and one cheesewring'. He had a herd of five 'milch cows', and butter and cheese worth £2. 10s. 'in store'.

Vancouver, writing in 1813, reckoned that in the South West a cow should produce 140 lb of cheese and 206 lb of butter a year. If all the milk of half a dozen cows (an ordinary number for a moderate farm then) went into cheese and butter, a farmer's wife would produce 120 7lb cheeses and 1200 lb of butter over the season, a never-ending task in the summer months, requiring a great deal of care and attention.

By the end of the eighteenth century there was some good cheese produced in east Devon at least. The valley of the Yarty around Yarcombe was known for its cheese, known in Exeter as Membury cheese. It was, as Marshall said, 'naturally a cheese district' and produced also Somerset cheeses, known there as Bridgewater cheese. By Marshall's day cheese was giving place to butter for the London market. However, right up until the 1920s, local skim- and whole-milk cheese was made and sold around Honiton, so good, it was said, 'that you could eat a pound of it at a time'. Many farms today are doing just what their predecessors had always done with surplus milk, but real, unseparated, scalded clotted cream with an authentic smoky taste is hard to get.

4.
Food

OUT TO WEEK beneath the trees,
Barley bread and vinid cheese,
Risty bacon as tough as a thong,
That's how Week boys git along!

This bit of doggerel came from Burrington in mid Devon and seems to be a mildly disparaging reference to the diet that folk from Week, a remote hamlet in the parish were accustomed to, and all they could manage. It may be a good description of the ordinary diet of the labourer or the smaller husbandman sometime in the past; rough coarse barley bread, cooked perhaps on the hearth and mostly discarded by the middle of nineteenth century in favour of white wheaten bread; scald milk cheese, old cheese veined with green cracks in the surface, and risty or rusty bacon, bacon streaked with brown from an incomplete cure. This was the very plain home-produced fare of many of the poorer farmhouses. A meal not much better than Week food was served up by the notorious Parson Froude of Knowstone who wished to offend an unbidden guest. This consisted of 'roast magpie, stewed bullaces [sour wild green plums] and Devon Blue Mould', a hard flavourless scald-milk cheese. This was a calculated insult, the worst food he could find. However in the end, warming to his guest, he relented and they dined eventually in some style on venison pasty, stewed fruit and cream, Stilton cheese and port.

Plain fare remained, however, the lot of the labourer. Marshall, in 1795, described the diet of the labourer and poorer husbandman as barley bread, skim-milk cheese and potatoes, whereas before the wars against France began, a labourer could afford wheaten bread and a little meat. The Revd James Windsor of Uffculme, writing in 1810, described the potato as the principal food of the poor, but says that before 1770, it was a garden crop only, left in the ground over winter till it was needed. Dean Milles' enquiry of 1750 has hardly a mention of potatoes but by 1770 it seems that potatoes were being grown extensively around Moretonhampstead, sold in Plymouth and their cultivation was spreading generally. By the time (1808) Vancouver wrote about Devonshire farming, the potato seems to have been universally grown in the county, and universally eaten in 'large quantities', particularly in the country, where they 'diminished the expenditure on other foods'. This change of diet must have been accelerated by the extortionate price of corn in some years during the period of the wars, 1795–1815. On a number of occasions townsfolk in the West Country rioted against the high price of bread and occasionally stormed the mills and took the flour and paid for it at what they called a 'just' price.

The Burrington jingle then, with no mention of 'tetties', may date from before 1770. It is likely to be not much older than that, since there is no mention of rye bread and rye was extensively grown in the South West up to the end of the seventeenth century. A great many inventories of the seventeenth century refer to rye, though it seems to have been grown in small acreages and less towards the end of the century. Some was probably always grown for thatching, as rye straw is the best for that purpose. Vancouver says that the lowest layers of thatch on old buildings were of rye straw, and that 'large fields of it were grown on the moors and commons'. The rector of Witheridge, hardly the best corn growing parish in Devon, echoes this judgement in answering Dean Milles. He said that very little rye was grown there but that it used to be grown in quantity on the wet moors seventy or eighty years before. At Plymtree, in the same year, rye was being once more grown but only for thatching straw. Highhampton was the only other parish in Devon where any rye was mentioned.

Rye was a crop for poor land; it would grow well where other cereals would fail. It was safe where folk depended on home grown grain, particularly on wet moory ground. Despite its virtues, it seems that rye bread was no longer eaten by 1750, its place being taken by barley bread. This may have been a matter of taste, but new varieties of barley and better husbandry practices may have contributed. It may also be that, with better transport and better roads, it was perhaps easier in moory country to bring in wheat and barley from more favoured areas, than try to grow those crops.

Barley bread was evidently preferred to rye, but it was still second best. It was used in Chulmleigh poorhouse when wheat bread was too expensive, though once, according to Marshall, it had been eaten by the middle classes. In 1739, after a very bad harvest and a viciously cold spring, the 'poor of Broadhembury were forced to eat bread made out of bad barley, which was like mire and black as mud, so that many perished through hunger and cold'. However, by the end of the next century matters had improved and one account of the labourer's life, written in 1882, claimed that 'he never now eats barley bread' and that the home baking of bread had largely ceased by then. Those who have eaten bread baked in the old clay or brick ovens say that no bread equals it, so something was lost in this change. By 1882 Britain was beginning to experience the flood of cheap North American hard wheat which produced the kind of white bread, baked at a high temperature in a steam oven, eaten today. The village corn mills that had ground the villagers' bread flour for centuries now became largely grist mills grinding cattle feed and villagers ate loaves baked from prairie grown wheat. Both rye and barley bread were a memory.

A form of porridge or water gruel was commonly eaten, known as 'girts'. The vicar of Landkey reported that the people of his parish prepared the grain for sale 'wherever water gruel is in use in His Majesty's dominions'. Elsewhere they were known as 'groats' and from this food derives, perhaps, the cherished corn 'grits' of the southern states of the USA.

The Week diet was that of the poorer sort of husbandman. His better-off neighbour, the yeoman, kept a better table. Thomas Tusser, writing from his knowledge of Suffolk and Essex, explains how diet changed with the seasons, as various foods became available. In Lent the farmer ate herrings and saltfish and after Easter, veal and bacon and Martinmas, beef (beef salted the previous autumn). Then came mackerel, and by midsummer, grassbeef (fresh beef) and pease, then at Michaelmas fresh herrings and fat mutton. By All Saints' Day there was pork and souse (pickled pig's feet and ears) and smelts and sprats, and then came Christmas.

> Good bread and good drink, a good fire in the hall,
> Brawne, pudding and souse and good mustard withal,
> Beef mutton and pork, shred pies of the best,
> Pig, veal, goose and bacon and turkey well drest,
> Cheese, apples and nuts, jolly carols to hear
> As then in the country is counted good cheer.

Christmas was a great feasting time, the twelve days of Christmas really meant twelve days holiday. The cows were mostly dry, the ewes had not started to lamb, wheat and rye were already sown, barley and oats could wait for the spring, most of last year's harvest was still in store and the hard days of February, March, and early April, when supplies of food and corn and hay and perhaps firewood ran low, were yet to come. The worst weather of the winter was also probably in the future – 'as the days get longer the cold gets stronger'. These first months of the year were the 'dying' months, when the parish registers often record the greatest number of deaths.

But all this could be forgotten at Christmas and the yeomen were expected to entertain, to lay out some of their stored up wealth:

> At Christmas be merry and thankful withal
> And feast thy poor neighbours, the great with the small.

Tusser continuously enjoins hospitality, and reminds the farmer of the need to feed his workman well. Ploughmen, he says should eat roast meat twice a week; he was also quite sure that ill-fed servants never worked well, and that they should be looked after, and well fed when they were ill.

He was doubtless something of an idealist both in his advice about servants and in his ideas of what food was available, but what he says about food can be confirmed to some extent from the inventories. Beef and bacon occur regularly; these were the hams and flitches hung from the ceiling, 'the roof meat', or stored in the cupboard or bacon settle. Pork occurs more rarely and mutton never at all. Sheep were certainly regarded first and foremost as suppliers of wool and it was not until the eighteenth century that breeders started to select sheep for their meat. Tusser certainly recommends the eating of mutton and the fattening of 'crones', as the old ewes were called. It may be that mutton was seldom salted, was therefore perishable and not recorded in the inventories. It was certainly being eaten in Devon by 1750 when the parson of St Marychurch, Torquay, reported that his parishioners lived on 'mutton, beans and Newfoundland cod'. This was probably greasy mutton from fattened up, broken-mouthed old ewes whose useful life as breeders was at an end. But in the last century mutton became a delicacy. Three-year-old mutton, from sheep reared very hard in mountain country, wintered and summered on the hills, was much in demand, the meat very lean and close grained and full of flavour. Sheep provided other delicacies; lambs' testicles and lambs' tails were commonly eaten in the days when the knife rather than the constricting rubber band was used to remove these objects. Traditionally, in folk memory, and in fact, starving men stole sheep to eat and it is likely that sheep were eaten when other meat was scarce. It is likely too that, rather in the same way, horse was eaten, as it was and is on the continent. In the debate about the merits of horses and oxen as plough beasts, it was always said in England that you could, at the end, at least eat the ox, but not, by implication, the horse. Despite, this it is almost inconceivable that the hungry did not eat horses when they could.

The Newfoundland cod mentioned at St Marychurch would have been familiar to Tusser. It was probably what he called 'haberden', the largest and best quality dried fish, which he says should be preserved dry in 'peasehaulms'. The Newfoundland Banks fisheries, where cod used to shoal in enormous numbers, were discovered by European fishermen early in Tusser's century and salt fish became very quickly staple diet of the Catholic countries in particular, for fish days and Lent and for the poor of all faiths, all over Europe. It was sold in the South West in the form of hard, brown, heavily salted lumps that barely looked like fish at all, or in recognizable whole-fish sized pieces. There were various ways of salting it and if it was dried initially in too hot weather, perhaps on stones, it lost its white colour and was described as 'burnt to the stone'. It also smelt pretty high, 'a rank smell, garlicky some modestly call it'. Devon folk were not so modest and called it vulgarly 'toerag'. In France it was forbidden to pour away the water in which cod had been soaked except at night, because of the smell. Despite this, it became a common food eaten by many until quite recently. It had certain virtues: it would keep, it was very nutritious, and it was cheap and easy to cook – poor folk's food. It is said that miners from Ashburton, who used to spend the inside of the week on the moor at their work living rough, took with them supplies of 'toerag' which they soaked in running water to remove the worst of the salt. Just how poor they were is suggested by the story of one of these men, who, it is said, lost his fish from a flood of water and had nothing else to live on for the rest of the week.

Salt fish, sometimes called 'fish in corr', figures quite often in the inventories along with other salted foodstuffs. Other fish were clearly readily available. The inventories refer to salmon nets and pilchard nets, and herring and mackerel swarmed along both coasts of the peninsula in the past. There is evidence of quite extensive coastal fishing in medieval times. In 1309 the fishermen of Stokenham on Start Bay had to transport three horseloads of fish from their own village to Stoke in Wiltshire, for the use of the lord of the manor there. This was presumably salted as the journey probably took the best part of a week. In Lent, the men of Stokenham had to 'station themselves by three rocks on the sea shore and with their own boats and tackle and at their own charges, take mullet' which the lord of the manor could buy at a low price. They also, it seems, caught salmon in Start Bay (for which they were paid nothing but a day's food), porpoise worth 1s. each, plaice at eight for 1d., bream at the same price, one skate for a 1d. and 'twelve pennyworth of conger for eleven pence.' This kind of fishing must have been usual all round the coast, and it seems likely that fresh fish would have been available at a price within a day's journey of the sea. Nowhere in Cornwall and not many places in Devon are further from the sea than that. Fish was sold as fresh; 'herrings fresh last night', was the cry in Paris – 100 miles from the sea – in the seventeenth century. Local fish, as well as Newfoundland cod, was probably salted and from the seventeenth century, at least, most of the West Country fishing villages sent ships to the Newfoundland banks in the spring, and welcomed them back finally in the autumn, just 'when the Parson reached Proverbs' in the lesson for the day.

West Country folk also ate seabirds and their eggs in some quantities. Young herring gulls, blackheaded gulls and kittiwakes were eaten, and some were caught alive and fattened on liver or corn. Puffins were thought to be too rank, 'fit only for servants', but the young of the cormorant were used to take the place of pigeons in squab pie. Parson Hawker believed that he had eaten seal meat at an inn in Boscastle when served up with what the landlady would only describe as 'meat and tetties'.

Salt fish and potatoes was a common meal on the farm and there were, of course, other vegetables available. Farmers grew large quantities of peas and beans in the past; the seventeenth-century inventories refer to these frequently. Tusser refers to 'hastings' peas and 'runcivall' – marrow fat – peas. These were specifically garden peas for the pot and for pease pottage, but field peas were grown too, known as hog's pease. 'Peasen fed' swine were the best. Peas were commonly grown in Devon in 1750, beans rather less commonly. These and oats were horse food, so, 'full of beans' and 'feeling his oats'.

'Beanes carrots and cabbages worth £1' appear in Robert Dicleg's inventory of 1643 and by the next century there was a very extensive trade in cabbages from Paignton. Here some 150–200 acres of very large cabbages were grown every year and 150 loads were carried each week from October to March to Newton Abbot, Tiverton, Exeter, Kingsbridge 'and even shipped along the coast' from London to Lands End and 'great quantities were sent to Newfoundland'. These must have been what are called today 'flatpolls': cattle cabbages, which can weigh 56 lb and will last a very long time in cold weather; they were clearly available all over south Devon in winter. They were not universally popular; one near-starving man, when offered cabbages free, said 'Cabbages? I want meat' and continued to starve.

Almost all familiar vegetables, parsnips, onions, spinach, lettuce, leeks, radishes and parsley were known by the early eighteenth century at least, but it is uncertain how common these were outside country house gardens or in market gardens growing for big towns. Egg Buckland grew carrots and turnips and cabbage for Plymouth in 1750s, and Ottery St Mary was known for its carrots. Stratton grew saffron for the famed Cornish saffron cakes and Mrs Deborah Tucker had some of this in her draper's shop in Exeter in 1695 as well as 'raisins of the sun', cloves, candy and fifteen loaves of sugar. These were probably for the well to do only. Incongrously, it was the poor of Stoke Fleming and Stokenham who were in 1750 eating another delicacy, that luscious vegetable sea kale, picked from Slapton Sands.

In 1808 Vancouver noted that leeks, 'which were so much in use', were commonly grown in cottage gardens and he thought that the Devonshire kitchen gardens and market gardens were surpassed only by those round London. But working farmers are not good about gardens and tend to leave them to the womenfolk, who have not enough time, or to 'granfer'. A few large farms, however, perhaps with a bit of labour to spare, have big cob walled gardens attached, once devoted to vegetables and wall fruit. Tusser knew all about raspberries ('respis'), strawberries and gooseberries; these were also familiar in their wild form to Carew in Cornwall. Fruit needed sweetening and preserving. Sugar appears in only three out of the 266 Devon inventories and two of those are of shopkeepers. It was known in Europe from the time of the Crusades, but was always a luxury until probably the late eighteenth century. Before that the only sweetener was honey; bees appear in inventories fairly frequently. 'Beeboles', hollows in walls to give shelter to the old straw hive or skep, survive in some garden walls. Baring-Gould refers to the powerful honey-based metheglin that he drank in the cottages of north-west Devon. Honey must have been plentiful for this to be made. Sugar has another use; it is, once boiled, a great preserver of fruit. Before the days of cheap sugar it was probably impossible to produce the shelves full of jam so beloved by housewives in the recent past.

Much of this food was seasonal, dear and probably unusual. It was bacon and bread that filled most bellies before the arrival of the potato. Bacon, salted and sometimes smoked, appears commonly in the inventories. Almost everyone had a pig or two. John Williams of Bratton Clovelly, left only £9 in goods including one little pig, and Joan Brownscombe, a fisherwoman of Dawlish, had three pigs and no other livestock among her goods valued at £15 in 1590. Most farmers fed their servants on fat bacon, and when labourers' cottages become usual they were often furnished with a small house at the end of the garden for the pig. Parson Hawker recounts how, in a fit of rather arrogant mischief, he and a parson friend released all the pigs from their hovels in Boscastle early one morning and the whole village filled up with stray pigs which he was told later, 'had rebelled and let each other out and they all be going to sea'! Pigs are omnivorous and could be fed cheaply on scraps; everyone kept one, and on fair-sized farms two were killed a year.

Pigs were fed to a vast size; the West Country simile is not 'fat as butter' but 'fat as a pig'. So fat were they that the resulting bacon was one eighth of an inch lean to an inch of fat. This was the diet of the labourer, who needed all the energy-producing fat for his eight to ten hour stint of walking behind a plough or making up a hedge. Once fat, pigs were stuck with a knife through the throat down into the heart, with little fuss if it was skillfully done. The blood was collected for black puddings. Once dead, the pig was carried from the sty on a pig form to the kitchen, or outhouse and hung up by the hind legs. Scalding water was then poured over it and the bristles removed with an object rather like a candle stick with a concave, sharp-edged bottom. This indeed held a candle at one end for singing off any surviving bristles and the sharp bottom was used to scrape off what remained down to the skin. After a day the pig was lowered on to a slab and cut up. The pig's head was stripped of its meat, which was pressed into a mould with onions and a bay leaf to be made into brawn. The feet and ears together made salted 'souse'. The gammons and hams were then salted in salting tryes or keeves, great earthenware troughs, glazed inside. There were many recipes for salting; some used bay salt (from the Biscay coast) or 'salt prunella' or just coarse salt to which saltpetre was almost invariably added. Sometimes beer, treacle, brown sugar or juniper berries were added to the cure. The meat lay in salt for three or four weeks, turned every day in the cure and the nooks and crannies of the meat rubbed hard with salt. Once cured it was often hung up the open chimney to smoke. This would preserve it better and give it a distinct flavour. Some farmhouses had separate curing chambers, burning oak sawdust, but these were fairly rare and confined to the bigger farms. A substitute for smoking was to pour 'essence of smoke' – pyroligneous acid or wood vinegar – over the meat. This was obtainable from chemists' shops. The joints were then wrapped in cloth and hung from the roof where they would keep for a year or more if properly cured.

The pig's insides also provided some delicacies. The fat was carefully removed from the intestines and stomach and rendered down for pure lard. The intestines were then turned inside out and washed thoroughly, using the fingers, in salted or running water and boiled. When completely clean they were cut into small pieces and fried with onions, pepper and salt and breadcrumbs. In the South West these were known as chitterlings, elsewhere as pig's fry. The intestines could also be cut up for sausages or white puddings, or mixed with blood, oatmeal and barley and made into black puddings. There was very little of the pig, probably only the bones, that could not be eaten. All this was once familiar workaday business known to every farmer's and labourer's wife and her responsibility. On the success of the curing and the skill of the housewife much of the year's diet depended: if she knew her job the family ate well.

Bread, bacon, salt fish and potatoes were everyday food but on special occasions folk could eat well. Farmer's wives were expected to produce roast meat and apple pie dinners on threshing days, when neighbours came to help; and at harvest they appeared in the fields with jugs of tea and cutrounds, cream and jam and currant cake, all in maunds covered over with white napkins. At the end of harvest, that peak of the farming year, there was another feast and at Christmas yet another with much drinking around the ashen faggot as it flared and cracked on the hearth.

Parson Hawker of Morwenstow conjured up, from memory perhaps, an epic dish in one of his tales of the past. The meal started with rye bread, 'wheat being a luxury unknown in Cornwall'. 'Rye loaves led the way, sweet and tasty to the final crust, barley bread and oaten cakes came forth in due procession' and last of all came a 'huge and mysterious pie, a hillock of brown dough that reeked like a small volcano with steaming puffs of savoury vapour'. Inside, 'when the massive crust which lay like a tombstone over the mighty dish was broken...conger eels, pilchards and oysters were mingled piecemeal, their intervals slushed with melted butter and clotted cream'. This was a Cornish pie and Hawker says the byword was 'Cornish cooks make everything into a pie' and that 'the devil never dared cross the Tamar or he would have verily been put under a crust'. Baring-Gould recommended another West Country delicacy, 'squab pie', originally made from young pigeons ('squabs'), probably taken from a culverhouse or dovecote. By his day pigeons were never used; instead, the pie consisted off mutton, veal, bacon, apple, onion, pepper and salt, a pilchard, Devonshire cream and occasionally newly fledged young rooks which, he said, were 'still highly relished' – all under a crust! Another Cornish dainty was 'stargazy pie', a pie crust through which pilchards gazed heavenwards, their heads just proud of the pastry. The most famous dish of all, fitting very well, even to its name, into the West Country pastry tradition, is, of course, the pasty. This was, by tradition, hand food, what a miner took down the mine with him for his midday meal, but it came to be made in all farmhouse kitchens. It should be a plate wide, of short pastry and filled with thinly sliced good beef-steak, onions, sliced potatoes and plenty of salt and pepper, all cooked slowly within a pastry case, so that the juice from the meat mingles with the potato and the pastry. Nothing like this can be bought today. If this was really ordinary farm food, then West Country folk ate well.

5.
Drink

SALT FISH, SALT BEEF, SALT pork, heavily salted butter, and salty cheese all helped to create, amongst those who worked on the land, what has been described as an 'oceanic' thirst. Tea, as a quencher of thirst, was too dear for ordinary folk until the end of the eighteenth century. If something better than water was wanted then there was a choice, in this country, of beer or cider. William Harrison described how he made three hogsheads of beer a month in his household, back in the sixteenth century. A parson's 'family' in those days was unlikely to have numbered less than ten; three hogsheads is nearly 200 gallons or 1600 pints, 160 pints per person, per month, or five pints a day for everyone in the family! The beer they drank was probably a fairly thin 'small' everyday beer, common in every household and even given to school boys in the last century, perhaps as a substitute for not very pure water. Queen Elizabeth's court drank 600 000 gallons of something like this every year.

A rough calculation of cider making in Devon in the middle of the eighteenth century showed that it is likely that Devon produced annually some 170 000 hogsheads, or nearly 10 million gallons. Devon had a population at that date of about 300 000. Assuming that no cider was exported this would give an annual consumption, per man, woman and child, of rather more than half a hogshead, perhaps thirty-five to forty gallons, that is about 300 pints a year or six pints a week, on top of any beer that was drunk. Children probably drank little cider, so working men consumed a great deal more than this. It is known that a lot of cider was exported from South Devon to Newfoundland, and to London, where some was used to adulterate wine. Even allowing for these exports, plainly a lot of cider was drunk. Other evidence shows that in Devon, as in Harrison's Essex, a lot of beer was made at home. Home brewing and farm cider-making were the rule in the country until probably a hundred and fifty years ago when breweries began to sell beer extensively.

Beer

Among the existing Devon inventories there are over thirty references to cider and apples and sixty-eight to beer and beer-making. Thirty of these refer to brew houses and malt houses, and these would seem to have been purpose-built outshots or lean-tos. This would be appropriate because they often contained a furnace or copper for the necessary hot water. There are also a few references to malt chambers, presumably within the farmhouse itself. To raise malt the sprouted grains of barley and, in the South West, wheat, oats or rye, required heat and a flat surface above the heat on which to spread the grains. In the fairly small kilns, or dryes as they were called, used by a farmer, the flat surface was provided by cloth made of hair or at least referred to often as a 'haire drye'. These occur quite frequently in the inventories. On these the grains were spread and a fire kindled beneath. A fire of straw was best according to Harrison. Raising malt was the housewife's business and there are references in the inventories to 'malt ready made' and new malt.

Normally it can be assumed that it was barley that was being malted, but there is one reference in the inventories to 'oaten malt'. Faith Knight of Whimple had old-fashioned tastes; she had six bushels of this 'oaten malt' amongst her goods in 1643. In a few other inventories the recording of 'oats and malt' together suggest that here too 'oaten malt' was meant. It is well known that in the fifteenth century in Devon oaten beer was made and Carew refers to it in his Survey of Cornwall. He says that the increase of barley tillage in his time 'amended the Cornish drink by converting that grain into malt, which (to the ill relishing of strangers) in former time they made only of oats'. John Hooker, a contemporary and probably friend of Carew, was much more forthright about this drink. He wrote – seemingly in words of disgusted experience – that despite the fact that the husbandmen on the edges of Dartmoor be

> very skilful in their husbandry and do dress their grounds very well, yet in the north part thereof about Okehampton, Hatherleigh, Iddesleigh, Chulmleigh and other places thereabouts, the oats which they sow be all spoiled oats, and the drink which they do make thereof is spoiled drink, for it be never so well prepared and dressed, yet what creature so ever do eat or taste thereof, be it man horse or hogge, it will make him to vomit and, for the time, very sick; nothwithstanding the people of that country, being used thereat, do endure the same very well; but yet if the said oats be shelded and converted to groats or oatmeal, it is very good and wholesome; the reason hereof no man can certainly define, whether it be by the greater mists, which commonly be there, or vapours, which the ground do yield, it is rather conjectured than certainly known.

A more contemptuous critic likened it to 'wash that pigs had wrestled dryn'! Nevertheless that is what the labourers on the Tavistock Abbey estates normally drank in the fifteenth century, replaced at the holidays of Christmas and Easter by the 'prime' or 'capital' brew made with wheaten malt. Barley was not much grown by the Tavistock monks and there is no mention of malting barley. Possibly it was a matter of local preferences since a century and a half later, when barley was commonly grown, Faith Knight was still making oat beer and probably she was not alone in her choice. Cornish beer improved and was clearly acceptable to strangers by the end of the century; Celia Fiennes drank 'very good bottled ale' in Penzance on her travels in 1698.

Very little is known about the types of beer that were brewed but there was one famous Devonshire beer, 'white ale', made at Kingsbridge, Slapton and elsewhere in the South Hams. This was still being drunk there in 1864. One ingredient was 'grout' which was 'a secret composition known only to a privileged few who made it and sold it to the ale brewers'. 'The malt liquor has much of the appearance of egg wine' and the beer was said to have been introduced by a German regimental surgeon to Dodbrooke 'some centuries ago'. The Rector of Dodbrooke took a tithe of white ale, so it is said, from his parishioners. The secret of this strong white ale is lost, though there have been attempts to revive its making. Perhaps German brewers still make such a drink.

Hops came into this country around 1534 according to the rhyme

> Hops, Reformation, Bays and Beer
> Came into England all in one year.

Thomas Tusser was quite familiar with hop growing and gave good advice about it. The inventories show that hops were available in Devon in the seventeenth century, though they are not mentioned very frequently. Three of the references occur in the inventories of 'gentlemen' and form one part of quite expensive items in a valuation. So George Yeo had 'wool, hops and salt worth 35s.' in 1607; John Bennett had 'wool, hops, leather thongs, girts worth £6' in 1625, and Leonard Yeo had 'wool, hops and feathers worth £7' in 1641. These read like bought items rather than the produce of the farm, so hop growing may not have spread to Devon by this time. Hops add a flavour to beer and help to preserve it and may have been originally quite a luxury. Later, mostly eighteenth-century, title deeds refer quite often to hop yards, or hop hays, as part of a farm, so it is likely that by then they were commonly grown and not confined, as they are today, to Kent and Worcestershire.

The inventories reveal quite sizeable household brewing operations. Nicholas Spicer, a yeoman of Heavitree near Exeter, had in his brewing house 'one furnace one great brewing keeve with eight other brewing tubbs, and one heating tub' and he had a cider house as well with 'three hogsheads of cider and four other hogsheads and two pipes'. Thomas Blampin of Gittisham had eleven beer barrels, two hogsheads, flagons and bottles, a furnace, sixteen vats and tubs, two old hogsheads and another couple of hogsheads in the cider house. Both of these men were well-off yeoman but Margery Butt, a widow of Dunkesell, had some malt in her small estate of £16 in 1554, and Salomon Westbeare, a weaver of Culmstock, had a malting hutch and malt, two vats and one tub amongst his goods worth £37 in 1592. Vats and keives and barrels and tubs were common items in households; some may have been just for storage of all sorts of goods, but most, probably, were for drink of some sort, good evidence of a great and universal thirst. Beer could be made anywhere where cereals were grown and in this it had an advantage over cider, which like the vine, needed the right climate. Much of Cornwall and most of Dartmoor and Exmoor were lamentably ciderless.

Cider

'Their orchards might well be styled their temples and apple trees their idols of worship.' This was Marshall's verdict on the devotion of Devonshire men to their cider. At Lustleigh, it was said that the men were far more interested in the prospects of the apple crop than in the corn crop and were never content till Ashburton fair day (first Thursday in June) had passed, since by then there was absolutely no danger of frost and their apple crop was assured. Apples were clearly on a par with corn, since almost the only two ceremonials commonly remarked on as being part of farm life were wassailing the apple trees after Christmas and 'crying the neck', carrying back home the last sheaf from the last field at harvest time, to hang at the roof until the next harvest.

Cider does not appear so often as beer in the inventories, but the evidence from Milles' enquiry about 1750 clearly shows the place it had assumed in West Country life. 'Every estate has an orchard', 'one acre to every £20', 'every cottage has some apples', were some of the responses to the Dean's queries and this kind of comment is frequent from most parts of the county. Even in Rose Ash, which, according to the Rector, was 'not a cider country', 'every tenement has an orchard'. It is possible to detect a note of regret in the Rector of North Molton's remark that his parish produced only 'poor meagre cider', or at Mariansleigh where there was 'little, bad cider' or at Challacombe and Countisbury up on Exmoor where there was 'no cider'. At nearby East Anstey there was little cider; it all had to be bought in. On the other hand the Rector of Marlborough near Salcombe said that the cider was 'as good as any in England'.

Some parsons clearly disapproved of cider drinking. At East Down, near Barnstaple, the reply was that the cider 'was good for nothing, on the evidence of the parish'. At Thelbridge all the questions about cider were heavily scored out and the Rector of Plympton replied, 'How much orchard? This ought not to be answered. An answer might be attended by ill consequences'. However, he may have been more concerned about excise duty than his parishioners' moral welfare. Later churchmen were to deplore the hold cider had over working men, particularly when it formed part of their wages. Farmers made cider for this purpose and kept their workmen happy with a plentiful supply. Sir John Acland, writing about 1850, said that working men spent one sixth of their wages on cider, since the farmers took that amount off the wages they paid them in return for unlimited supplies. It is said that, when hoeing swedes or mangolds, the way to make sure that the work was done as quickly as possible was to have a jar of cider at both ends of the rows. It is unlikely that the rows were very well hoed by the end of the day! Men took cider to work with them; the smallest barrel, the firkin, was for carrying at the belt into the fields. One old retired farmer living alone did not think two hogsheads (130 gallons) by any means too much for a year's personal drinking. Men sometimes acquired a great craving for cider that could not be stifled. One farmer kept a good stock of barrels for his men, but noticed that the level in the barrels was far lower than it should be. The door to the cider house had an inside 'apse' that could be opened by inserting a finger into a hole. Here he fixed a gin trap with the jaws against the hole and caught his man. Many regarded taking cider, like scrumping apples and smuggling, as no sin.

Cider even got into politics. In 1763 it became a hotly contested political issue. The government passed a law exacting a tax of 4s. a hogshead on cider, that is a surcharge of some twenty to twenty-five percent. This caused enormous protests wherever cider was drunk. In Devon a committee was appointed 'by a general meeting of the County to superintend the application for the repeal of the duty'. In Honiton, however, local folk had a chance to express their opinions in actions not words. A bye-election was due and the local candidate Sir George Yonge, of Escot in Talaton, very much opposed to the tax, was contesting the seat with a London merchant Anthony Bacon, of whom no-one knew anything except that it was rumoured that he supported the duty. The historian of Honiton, Farquharson, wrote:

> The West of England was in a state of ferment owing to the proposed tax. Mr Bacon was thought to be in favour of this. The report spreading, the country folks came in and a fight ensued between them and Mr Bacon's supporters. So desperate was the encounter that the streets ran with blood and the water of the River Gissage was tinged!

In 1766, after a memorial to the government from Sir George Yonge himself, the tax was repealed. This needed a celebration and Sir George provided a sheep to be roasted and seven hogsheads of cider. 'A fine ox, adorned with flowers and gilt apples, was led through the town attended by drums and fifes with a green flag bearing a scroll "Yonge and Liberty and no Cider Tax".' There were disturbances elsewhere in the West Country, and the government bowed to the cider drinkers, most of whom had no vote but strong opinions.

All pubs sold rough, locally made cider, and in country districts small, often isolated, probably unlicensed, cider houses were common. They were deplored by the gentry, but in 'unsquired' parishes they could appear in some numbers. Broadhembury, a large village with resident gentry for some generations had and has one pub only. Neighbouring Payhembury, an open village, smaller, with no large landlord, had at one time five, perhaps six.

South and east Devon were great cider countries, producing, clearly on a commercial scale, great numbers of hogsheads annually, each containing roughly sixty-five gallons. The Milles enquiry provides figures of a sort. At Bere Ferrers production was two thousand hogsheads, Paignton 'at least four thousand', at Berry Pomeroy two to three thousand. These parishes were some of the biggest producers. At the other end of the scale was

Buckland in the Moor with twelve hogsheads, Bittadon with one acre of orchard and Mary Tavy with two to three hogsheads produced every year. These small figures were cider for home consumption presumably. Only the highest and coldest of parishes like Challacombe and Countisbury reported no cider making at all. Yields can be worked out at roughly two to three hogsheads per acre, with here and there as much as ten. Paignton, with perhaps eight hundred to a thousand acres of orchard and all the other large producing parishes, must have been embowered in floods of pink and white scented blossom, a sight to see in April and May when all the trees were in bloom. Much of this cider was, of course, sold and farmers were said to drink the worst cider they produced and sell the best. One quite small farmer boasted of making fifty to sixty hogsheads which he sold to the local publicans. Cider was clearly a commercial farm crop, and probably a profitable one.

Knowledge of cider goes back a long way; it is an old drink, known for centuries. In 1174 cider (*sicera*) and perry (*piratum*) cost the 'fermer' of Windsor 6s. 8d. In the Lollard English Bible, of the early fourteenth century, still preserved in the chained Library at Hereford, the word used for 'strong drink' is 'cider'. Hence its nickname the 'Cider Bible'. Hereford was then, and of course still is, a county where strong drink was, first and foremost, cider. In France, cider reached the Cotentin and the Caen region in Normandy in the eleventh or twelfth century and may have come to this country with the Plantagenets. It is just as likely however that the discovery and making of cider was quite spontaneous in both countries. Wherever apples grow well and the surplus is liable to rot and ferment, cider will be made.

It was certainly being made in Devon by the thirteenth century. Thirty casks of cider from the Courtenay estates in Devon, at Tiverton, Plympton and Exminster, were sold at 11s.–12s. a barrel in 1286. The Abbot of Tavistock had a cider press at Plymstock from the end of the fourteenth century. This was also used by his tenants for a fee, and cider from here was shipped up the Tamar to Morwellham for the use of the monks at Tavistock itself. By the seventeenth century apples and presses occur fairly frequently in the inventories. In 1646 Jane Richards of Rewe had an apple chamber and apples worth £3, a pound house with 'an apple pound or press with the trugg stone and with all things therunto belonging, one great vat and three hogsheads' and she had sold some apple trees for £4. She had a drink house and a malt house and a malt chamber also, appropriately fitted up with tubs and 'haire cloths' and a screen mill. Around the farm she had in all some thirty barrels of one size or another. She died a rich woman worth £456. Rather less rich were Henry and Joan White of Plymtree, who had in 1643 'one stone and trough to break apples two wrings with levers and keys complete, seven vats two bowls and one tunner' and 'fourteen hogsheads at home and abroad'. These were all at a property they owned at Tale in Payhembury and they were evidently in the business of selling cider as they had casks 'abroad', that is in other folks' houses. Their joint inventory valued their goods at £109. Cider was not, however, just drunk by the rich. In 1569 Robert Catlake of Rewe had apples worth 4s. in his estate of £7 and

Richard Emmet of Staverton had a pipe of cider worth 20s. in an estate of £18 in 1590.

The inventories give some sort of indication of how cider was made. Two processes were involved. One was crushing the apples to a pulp, and the second was pressing that pulp to extract the juice. Celia Fiennes gives a description, maybe the first, of this process. Writing of Somerset and the country about Lyme Regis, she remarked upon

> plenty of apples and pears, but they are not curious in planting the best sort of fruit which is a great pity; being so soon produced and of such quantities they are likewise as careless when they make cider; they press all sorts of apples together else they might have as good cider as in any other parts even as good as the Herefordshire; they make great quantity of cider their presses are large; so as I have seen a cheese as they call them which yielded two hogsheads; they pound their apples, then lay fresh straw on the press and on that a good lay of pulp of the apples then turn in the ends of the straw over it all round and lay fresh straw then more apples up to the top.

The crushing of the apples was most recently done by an apple mill. It was a small cylinder, a drum with teeth fixed to the outside, mounted on a framework and turned by horse power at some speed through gearing. Into a large funnel above this the apples were poured to be crushed by the rotating teeth and the pulp was deposited at ground level. This involved some fairly sophisticated gearing and cog wheels and an iron cylinder. The use of iron for this suggests that this was a development that occurred in the eighteenth century at the earliest, though the cog wheels and geared drive were probably well within the scope of any good millwright who produced similar objects for use in a corn mill. Before iron cylinders became available, apples were crushed in a circular stone trough in which a heavy stone wheel ran. The power for this was provided by horses harnessed to the wheel walking continuously in a circle. This is the 'trugg stone' and 'the stone and trough to break apples' of the inventories. In 1750 the reply to Dean Milles' enquiry from Paignton refers to 'engine pounds' and 'stone troughs' and the same contrast between the two, 'stone pounds' or 'engine pound' comes from nearby St Marychurch. It is not clear exactly what is meant by the word engine, but it is probable that the geared iron drum or cylinder is being referred to, as the stone trough and stone wheel hardly deserve the name. Stephen Shute of Crediton insured his pound and engine in 1758 as did John Channon of Cullompton in 1760. So if this is a correct interpretation, the geared cylinder was known in Devon by the middle of the eighteenth century.

Both of these types of apple crusher would have been housed in round houses or pound houses. These rather elegant buildings still survive in some numbers, though turned to other uses. They normally take the shape of five sides of an octagon built up against a barn wall. There was a central large post around which the horses walked continuously turning a horizontal wheel geared to a drive. This could crush apples or it could power a barn thresher or other machinery. A round house is not therefore necessarily associated with crushing cider apples, as it had other functions. The word 'pound' can also be confusing; some pounds certainly crushed apples, but some names containing the word 'pound' refer to an enclosure for impounding stray animals with which many villages were provided.

Once crushed, the apple pulp was placed on the bed of the press. When this is done the juice starts to run immediately before any pressure is applied. Placed to receive it was a half barrel from which the juice was poured through the 'tunner', or funnel, in to the waiting barrels. The pulp was made into a cheese just as Celia Fiennes describes, using alternate layers of pulp and straw – oat straw was the best – and tucking the ends of the straw into the pulp. Without the straw the pulp would just squash flat, 'quat down', under pressure. This cheese was built up to some height, perhaps four or five feet, before pressing and once fully pressed the edges were sliced off with a hay knife and placed on top for more pressing. Not a scrap of juice was wasted. Presses were of various kinds. One was the single screw press with wooden threads and power exerted by a large bar like a capstan bar; another was the double screw press, with each threaded upright fitted with a rotating handle that forced down one side of the press at a time. Presses needed a very strong base and also a massive cross beam above to resist upward pressure. Despite this, pressing cider sometimes caused the roof of the pound house to rise bodily!

There were probably one or two of these presses in each parish. Every farm had its orchard but most took their apples to a neighbour for pressing. The apples started to fall in October or November and were eventually shaken down and piled by shovel or hand into heaps until the brown rot showed. All sorts of unmentionables went into the heap with the shovel. Pigs and cows and poultry all love apples, and it was difficult to keep them out of the orchard. When a suitable time could be arranged, the apples were carted off in bags to the press where the owner took charge. It was a social occasion; there was newly made cider to be sampled judiciously, and old mature cider from last year to be tapped, comparisons between apples, and between seasons, and between different farms' orchards, all to be made in the only way available. It was impossible to make cider without a lot of refreshment, particularly when muscle power was needed on the press. Cider fermented naturally, no yeasts were needed, and the heady scent of fermenting cider could be smelt far off. Cider-making was for many the crown of the year, days of hard enjoyable work enlivened by good company and good drink, with promise of future contentment and joy.

Before any cider-making could take place the barrels had to be prepared for the new batch. The dregs of farm cider – one magnificent word for these was the 'snarlygogs' – formed a thick yellow, curd-like, ropey substance in the barrel. The only way to get rid of this was to insert a good length of chain through the bung hole, hang on to one end, pour in boiling water and roll the barrel around till the dregs could be broken up and poured out. Empty barrels had to be tested for leaks and the iron hoops driven home to tighten up dried out barrel staves. Looking after empty barrels was always a problem. If they were left out in the rain they rotted; if they were kept indoors they dried out and leaked. The right answer was to keep them indoors and then remember to throw buckets of water over them at intervals. Leaky barrels, newly filled with precious freshly-made cider, were a disaster to be avoided at all costs.

Once the barrels were full the cider was allowed to work. The bung was left off and all the impurities in the cider, straw, stalks, pips, skin, dead woodlice and earthworms, and anything else, erupted and worked their way to the surface in a great scummy froth to the accompaniment of extraordinary gurgles and sighs and the breaking of bubbles. All the scum was removed, or sank to the bottom, and the barrel had to be kept filled to the brim with water, cider from another barrel or with anything else deemed suitable. When it had stopped working after a couple of weeks, when in fact a candle would burn clearly in the bung hole, it was bunged down absolutely tight. Any air allowed in would turn the cider to vinegar. Sometimes raisins or brandy were added for flavour and latterly chemicals were used to cut the fermentation. An old method of doing this was to burn a piece of cloth dipped in brimstone suspended inside a partly filled bunged barrel.

Once a barrel was tapped it had to be drunk quickly or decanted into smaller barrels and bunged up again. The best cider was racked once or twice and fined with isinglass but most rough, home-brewed cider did not get this treatment. Even so, home-made rough cider, pale clear green or pale yellow, kept as cold as possible, fresh from tapping, is a drink hard to beat, especially with roast or grilled meat or strong cheese. It could also be extremely strong, and it was often very cheap. In 1750 fair cider was 2d. to 3d. a gallon 'at the pounds mouth' when a man's wages were perhaps 7s. a week. In 1965 it was possible to buy farm cider for 8s. (40p) a gallon or 1s. (5p) a pint. Since then excise duty has been imposed on any quantity of cider made, this time with no protests.

At one period in the past Devonshire cider acquired a very poor reputation. What was known as Devonshire colic, severe digestive trouble, was put down to cider and a long debate eventually showed that this was due to the use of lead in lining the presses and troughs. Colic was in fact lead poisoning and this was discovered by Doctors Huxham and Baker in about 1760. Quite a number of learned pamphlets were issued on this subject at about that date, and there were various theories, but eventually the truth was discovered and the use of lead discontinued. That did not stop a general disapproval of cider, largely because of its other effects. Marshall wrote:

> the drunkeness, dissoluteness of manners and the dishonesty of the lower class might well be referred to the baleful effects of cider which workmen of every description make merit of stealing; and what is noticeable the effects of cider on working people appear to be different from that of malt liquor. Give a Kentish man a pint of ale and it seems to invigorate his whole frame, he falls to his work again with redoubled spirit. But give a Devonshire man as much or twice as much cider and it appears to unbrace and relax rather than to give cheerfulness and energy to his exertions.

It is said that cider goes to the knees and tends to stupefy; nevertheless many great cider drinkers lived to a good age. One old man of eighty-six said, 'they say cider kills slowly, it must be monstrous slow, I have been drinking cider since I was six'. What probably deserved disapproval was the paying of wages with cheap cider which did little for a man's family and kept the man himself dependent once he had acquired a taste. In the 1860s when labourers real wages in Devon were the lowest in the country, there was hardly another source of enjoyment for the labouring man.

'Necessity': still liquor

Devon had a cider spirit like Norman Calvados, though little is known about it. It was known as 'still liquor' and the making of it, in recent times at least, was entirely illegal, and attracted a massive fine. Nevertheless it was made in farm houses and cider houses in east Devon until quite recently.

The material used was the 'snarlygoggs', the sticky yellow mass found at the bottom of emptied cider barrels. Vancouver says that the dregs were filtered through barrass (or canvas) bags and the separation of pulp from juice in the dregs was made easier by adding fresh bullock's blood to the pulp. This could then be added to the ordinary cider or it could be distilled. Sometimes no such separation was attempted and the snarleygoggs were distilled as they came out of the barrel. The still was a 'porridge pot with a tin head communicating with a straight pipe, passing through a hogshead of water'. The liquor was passed twice through this and was extremely 'empyreumatic'. In Marshall's time it was known as 'necessity' since without a dose of this, the colic could not be cured and it was also said to be a good reviver of cattle. The treatment for colic caused 'obstinate costiveness for several days, accompanied by excruciating pain'. It was kill or cure, 'first the loss of use of the limbs, then in the loss of life, if the deprivation of life can be said to be a loss under circumstances so distressing'. Despite Marshall's appalling verdict 'necessity' continued to be made and sold until the 1920s and maybe later. Later stills had curly spiral tubes passing through water and a milk churn was a good pot for boiling. All this could be quickly dismantled and hidden if the constable paid a visit. The smell gave the game away; distilling this stuff gave off a smell like burning rubber tyres, detectable some way off. When the policeman called to search for the still he was asked to read his warrant. This took long enough for the still to be dismantled, the 'worm' of tubes hidden, and the brew poured down the drain. Illegal distilling was another 'crime' thought completely blameless by country folk and stories reveal that the constable felt just the same and very few stills were found or convictions made.

It is possible that distilling has a long history. John Fisher of Down St Mary had a still worth 12s. amongst his belongings in 1623; Edward Gould had a still and a limbeck worth 20s. in 1628 and Mary Bradford of Colyton had one worth 10s. in 1674. Most of the stills in the inventories were owned by gentry. Of course they may not have been used to produce spirit from cider, but it is the obvious and most plentiful source. In Europe brandy was regarded as a medicine and a miraculous preserver of youth until the fifteenth century, and was only distilled commercially as Cognac in the seventeenth. John Fisher was really quite well up with the times on his farm at Down St Mary in 1623. It was also possible to buy foreign spirits; in 1665 Henry Byrd, a merchant of Dartmouth had, among his stores, five cases and nine bottles of 'strong waters'.

Wine

There were no vineyards in the South West after the Middle Ages until very recent times. The monasteries may have experimented, and even succeeded, in the drier summers common in those times. A number of fields bear the name Vineyard and it is not clear what this may mean, but some West Country people drank wine. Joan Sparke, a widow, who died in 1645, seems to have been a wine merchant or the widow of one. She had in her cellar, for instance, two pipes of canary, seven butts of sherry, seven hogsheads of wine vinegar, one hogshead of red wine, two hogsheads of claret, two hogsheads of sack, a remnant of tent (spanish wine) and part of a butt of Malaga. A good deal of her wine was 'decayed'. Her inventory gives no indication of where she lived but most probably it was Exeter. She had about thirty-five barrels of wine of one size or another in her cellar, worth over £225. She was well off; she had a house of nine rooms, apart from a kitchen and cellar. Clearly there was no lack of trade. She died worth £459.

Water

Giving water to your workmen at harvest time, or at threshing, provoked the utmost scorn and did a man no good if he wanted help later. One old teetotaller, when asked for drink one hot harvest day, pointed unwisely to the stream, 'have as much as you can drink!'. But water was in some ways important. There were, in a great many parishes, special springs for curative, medicinal, or even magical purposes. Many springs were said to be good for eyesight, gout, or for fertility in women. These were locally well known and sometimes a well head was constructed around them. The place names Holwell and Halwell, and Ladywell and Blindwell, not uncommon in field names, record such holy and useful springs. Some are associated with saints, perhaps indicating pre-Reformation recognition and use. At Heavitree a Brides' spring is recorded as early as AD 938. St Budoc's well at St Budeaux (Plymouth) was for infertile wives. Eyewell at Seaton and perhaps all the Blindwells were for eyesight. At Combe Martin, St John's spring, recognized in 1750 at least, was bottled and sold as 'Coulsworthy water' for thirty years or so at the beginning of this century. It was found to be good for over-indulgence, gout and almost everything else! There were at least 220 such notable wells in Devon and probably as many, if not more, in Cornwall where wells are often associated with the Celtic saints and their churches. These were all curative in some way and how they acquired their reputation and what distinguished them from any other well or spring is not clear. 'Well' in West Country dialect is a place from which water 'welled out' and not just a carefully lined deep hole in the earth. Such wells would have been familiar and useful to all local people.

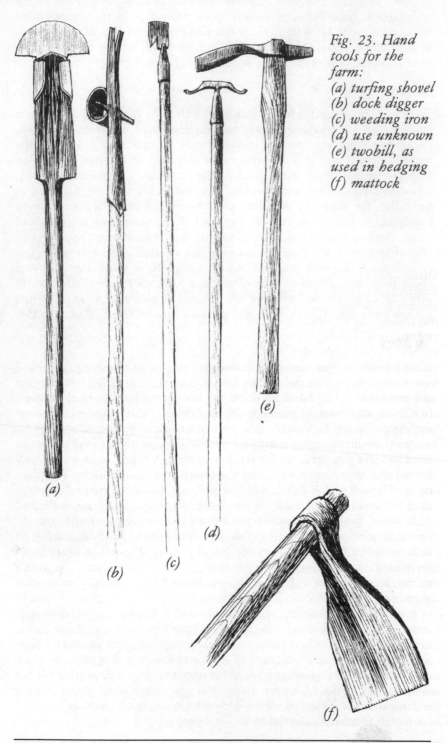

Fig. 23. Hand
tools for the
farm:
(a) turfing shovel
(b) dock digger
(c) weeding iron
(d) use unknown
(e) twobill, as
used in hedging
(f) mattock

Part II:
Farm Work

6.
'The Best Husbandry'

OLIVER CROMWELL SAID THAT HE had been in all the counties of England, and that the husbandry of Devon was the best he had seen. He was in Devon from October 1645 to perhaps January 1646, so he saw the county largely after corn harvest, but during apple harvest, hedging and winter ploughing time, and when the meadows were being watered. He was a country gentleman; he knew the land, and he may well have visited Devon at other times and based his judgement on more than one winter visit. He is unlikely to have been entirely wrong. It is of interest to work out what might have attracted his approval. A hundred and fifty years after 1646, William Marshall had some very interesting things to say about farming in the South West. He wrote that Devon and Cornwall, and the western parts of Somerset and Dorset, form a 'natural department of the Kingdom' and that 'this was under a course of rural management, which differs from that of the island at large, and whose basis has a different origin'. He was struck by the fact that 'Damnonian husbandry', as he called it, 'should not have assimilated over the centuries with that of the whole island'. He then listed twenty-eight practices peculiar to the South West and went on to say that the husbandry of the two counties was 'as distinguishable from that of the body of the island, as if the peninsula they form had been recently attached to it'. He thought this husbandry had defects, but also excellencies that could well be copied in the rest of the country.

Clearly, south-western farming was different and unusual. First and foremost, by the seventeenth century, the land was very largely enclosed. The South West was not unique in this respect, Essex and Kent were enclosed too, but much land in England still lay in great unhedged open fields. With a few exceptions, Braunton and Boscastle for instance, there were no great open fields with their intermingled strips in the South West: the land was divided into small fields with high hedgebanks, much as it is today. In these enclosed fields, a man could farm as he wished, subject only to the terms of his lease. He could be 'bold of his own' as Tusser said, and he did not have to conform to the communal rules and regulations of the open field village, so common in much of the rest of the country. He could grow crops of his own choosing, harvest them at his own convenience and graze his animals on his own fields apart from those of his neighbours. None of these things were normally possible in open-field country. All the agricultural writers in the seventeenth century agreed that enclosure was the *sine qua non* of agricultural improvement. Enclosure made it easier to introduce improvements. On their enclosed fields south-western farmers practised 'ley farming' or 'alternate husbandry'. They did not divide their land strictly into grassland and arable, but alternated it between the two, ploughing up grass to crop it for two or three years with corn, and then laying it down to grass for seven to ten years, before ploughing again. This is in total contrast to open-field husbandry, where it was common to grow two corn crops, and then fallow the field for a year before more corn was sown. Grass under this system was confined largely to the wet meadows and the village common, where all the village animals grazed together. The wasteful full year's fallow was unknown in the South West; instead ley farming was a flexible system, that ensured fertility by the ploughing in of well-trodden and well-grazed grass and clover swards. It is now proven common practice in the country as a whole.

To plough rough moory grassland and the tough sward of a good temporary ley, Devonshire farmers had devised the practice of beat burning, or, as it was known in the seventeenth century, 'Devonshiring'. The sward was pared off, dried and burnt; the ashes could then be mixed with other manures and spread onto the fields. A full account of this technique is found on pages 107–10.

It is only useful for grassland, hence it is associated necessarily with alternate husbandry or ley farming, in which grass is regularly ploughed. It played no part in ploughing ordinary arable land. Having ploughed and 'Devonshired', south-western farmers spread a variety of dressings including calcareous sand from the coast, lime and marl. Their leases forbade them to plough land without a dressing of sand or lime or dung, and this last was applied in considerable quantities, using all the human and industrial wastes of the towns and villages. Leases also restricted the amount of land that was under crops at any one time, seldom more than a quarter of the ploughable land, the rest having to be in grass.

This grassland was equally well looked after. Seed mixtures were not just the sweepings of the hay talat but contained rye grass – Devon eaver – and white clover. The small fields enabled rotational grazing to be practised, shifting stock from field to field. The hedgebanks provided shelter and timber. On the watered and manured meadows sheep and cattle got an early bite of grass in the cold spring of the year.

This system of husbandry was certainly well established in the seventeenth century and probably long before that. It was the husbandry that Cromwell saw and it was evidently sufficiently productive to elicit his approval, and sufficiently different to call forth Marshall's verdict. It is possible to measure this success roughly. The yield of certain cereal crops can be calculated between the fifteenth century and the late eighteenth century from a variety of sources. In the fifteenth century the monks of Tavistock Abbey were getting better yields from their poorish lands, using this system of husbandry, than were being obtained from the better cornlands of Kent and Cambridgeshire. By 1750 Devonshire farmers were obtaining yields of wheat and oats nearly treble that obtained at Tavistock two and a half centuries before. They did this using only the husbandry practices described above. Cromwell's verdict would seem to be justified.

By the later nineteenth century, however, agricultural writers had a low opinion of south-western farming. They based their opinions on what was the received wisdom of the agricultural revolution, the Norfolk four course rotation, the regular growing and folding of turnips, the continued use of the fallow, the use of bought manures and virtual separation of arable from grassland. Modern practice during and since the second world war would suggest that they were wrong, that the well-fed long ley was as good or better basis of fertility for cropping than the four course. Other criticisms, of weedy unhoed turnips, old-fashioned machinery, small farms, etc. had more validity, but West Country farmers learned to hoe turnips, iron machinery makers appeared in every town and farms gradually grew larger. When, in the 1870s, the agricultural depression, induced by cheap corn imports, bankrupted many up-country farmers, the effect in the South West was much less severe. Here, farmers turned their corn land to grass, as they were used to doing, and took advantage of the new railway system to send fat cattle, pigs and sheep, butter, new potatoes, flowers and fruit to the big markets in the east. Most of these farmers still operated on a small scale, using very largely the methods of their forefathers, making cider and cream, keeping a pig for the house, growing a little corn and a few turnips and swedes, keeping both sheep and cattle, still spreading sand and burning beat, sharing the work of the harvest, eating harvest dinners, but doing most of the work on the farm themselves.

7.
The Fields of the Farm

The origin of fields

West Country fields and their hedgebanks provoke comment and curiosity. The fields are small and irregularly shaped, the hedges that surround them are huge earth banks, surmounted by a growing living hedge. The fields might form a pattern around the farmstead, which is frequently on its own, isolated in the midst of its fields. Here and there are big villages, the main street lined with former farmhouses. However, it is the patchwork of small fields, lonely hamlets and ancient farms, seemingly in a centuries-old sleep, perched above the deep combes and tucked into the furzy hillsides, that makes the landscape of Devon and Cornwall so attractively different and distinctive.

It is in the main a medieval landscape; the fields were laid out and enclosed, and the banks built at least five hundred years ago for the most part, and some must be a great deal older than that. It is not difficult to imagine a man and his family in the distant past, finding no room in his home parish, seeking land for a farm in the uncultivated waste, looking for somewhere where water, meadow, arable, and a bit of woodland would be to hand and setting about the business of clearing that waste, little by little, to grow corn and make hay to feed his family and livestock. Many farms in the South West must have originated in this way. Farm names like Newcott or Newton may identify them.

The first task would be to clear some land for ploughing. This would demand the felling and grubbing of woodland, and the cutting and burning of scrub. Then followed the first breaking of the ground with an ox plough, or with a breast plough, pushed and pulled by the brute strength of the farmer and his family. The acreage that could be cleared before crops had to be sown in the winter or spring would be small, an acre or two, and to protect this from stock some sort of hedge had to be made, initially out of the felled timber. The shape of such fields would be fixed by the presence of immoveable boulders and unfellable trees, ever running springs and unploughable cleaves. The result would be odd-shaped and irregular. Fields just like this can be seen everywhere in the South West and they must be the result of such a process. This process of clearing the waste and tilling it continued well into the last century. On Dartmoor, Bronze Age reaves, low banks some three thousand years old that divide the moor, often merge with the familiar hedgebanks of the enclosed fields of the farm. Devon and Cornwall still abound in moory commons, 'waste' in the old sense. In the valleys of the Blackdowns in East Devon, and on the edge of every bit of common, men were taking in a bit of waste acre by acre, tilling it and building on it squatters' cottages, right into the last century. By tradition this building was allowed if some sort of chimney was raised, and fire kindled within twenty-four hours. Sometimes such settlement was a communal effort and in medieval times landowners planted groups of men on uncultivated land. In 1086 Devon was well settled; a map would show few large gaps other than Dartmoor and Exmoor, but between each settlement must have lain acres and acres of waste awaiting the axe and the plough. The fields that were cleared and created in this way are clear to see.

However, this cannot be a complete explanation of field patterns in the South West. Not uncommon at all is a pattern of regular, sometimes narrowly rectangular, fields lying in more or less parallel ranks. These must have quite a different origin from the piecemeal clearance of the waste, as they appear to be laid out and planned, formally. It is also possible to see where the fields that form this pattern have been amalgamated to form rather bigger rectangular fields. This rectangular pattern is, in fact, a relic of the strips and furlongs of the open fields, of what was once called 'champion' country. This type of landscape was once common in the Midlands and eastern parts of England.

In 'champion country' the farms lay in big villages surrounded by three or so huge fields divided into hundreds of strips of land, few more than a couple of acres in size. These strips were grouped in named furlongs, and a man had the land of his farm scattered in each of the three fields, divided amongst the furlongs. The strips were usually narrowly rectangular, because it was easier with a clumsy eight-ox team to plough in long narrow strips than in the square. Such a shape involved less turning of the team during a day's ploughing. Traditionally, a day's work was an acre, a furlong (furrow long) long (220 yds) and a chain (22 yds) wide: ten times as long as broad. Most of the land was arable: wheat followed fallow, that followed spring corn, that followed wheat, and so on, in a rotation that did not allow for much diversification of cropping. Men very largely had to follow the rules of the village in what they cropped and when they harvested. Hay was cut in the meadows which, too, were in small strips, and animals were grazed as a common flock all together on the common, or over the open field strips after harvest, or in the fallow year.

This system, so common in the country as a whole until the eighteenth century, once existed in the South West; at both Boscastle and Braunton it is still practised after a fashion. The shape of the old open field strip is still preserved and fossilized in the narrowly rectangular fields that still survive on many farms in the South West. Here the strips were at some time enclosed and hedged from the open fields, on which originally no hedge or fence divided strip from strip.

In the Axe valley, the open fields were enclosed into small fields by the early fourteenth century for the efficient and flexible grazing of cattle and sheep. East Devon was already by that date a pastoral farming district, 'on the green side'. The South Hams was always an arable area. Crops could be grown well in open-field strips, and enclosure was less important to farmers. It came later, in the fifteenth century, when the population declined and there was land going begging, so it became easy to exchange and enclose strips to form the present-day fields. At Kenton, in the Exe valley, open fields lasted even longer, partly in response to the good market for corn in nearby Exeter. Some similar history of enclosure related to the local farming practice may be applied to all the other parts of the South West that were once under open field, where land was held 'by landscore' as it was termed in Devon, or by 'stitchmeal' in Cornwall. Why Braunton and Boscastle remain unenclosed has not been determined. Curiously, the size of the fields in the Axe valley and the South Hams seems to relate to the date they were enclosed. East Devon fields are generally noticeably smaller and more irregular than those in the South Hams. Fields in the South Hams are squarish or broadly rectangular, suggesting readily how strip was added to strip and then enclosed.

There were reasons for this early abandonment of open field in the South West. Firstly, an enclosed, hedged landscape (once known as 'several') allowed flexibility, unlike the regulations and rules of the open field. Thomas Tusser, who had farmed in Suffolk (another enclosed county) during the mid sixteenth century, was clear about this.

> More plenty of mutton and beef, corn butter and cheese of the best,
> More wealth anywhere to be brief, more people more handsome and prest
> Where find ye (go search any coast) than that where enclosure is most.
> More profit is quieter found where pasture in 'several' be,
> Of one silly acre of ground than 'champion' maketh of three
> Again what a joy is it known, when men may be bold of their own.

In 'several' country a man could farm and feed his own land as he liked, choosing his own crops and rotations, and his stock could be pastured and bred away from contact with other men's animals.

More important, probably, was the fact that in the South West there was plenty of common upland grazing on which to pasture animals in summer. In champion country the only grazing lands for animals, apart from fairly small commons, were the corn fields after harvest, the fallow, and the meadow after hay harvest. All these had to be available to the village livestock, and a man could not enclose his own strips in the open fields without depriving his neighbours of grazing. So enclosure was a difficult communal problem in champion country. When Midland open fields were eventually enclosed in the eighteenth and nineteenth century, a totally new map was drawn and surveyed of the village farmlands, with large regular fields separated by thorn hedges. It was an entirely different landscape to that created by the medieval enclosures in the South West, which might be described as a peasants' landscape.

The South West did have some land which was enclosed in the eighteenth and nineteenth centuries, but this was common land used for rough grazing, not open-field arable. It was duly surveyed and laid out in accordance with contemporary ideas, straight wide roads and large squarish fields. This is a third, fairly rare, type of south-western field, unlike the other two and instantly recognizable as part of a Parliamentary enclosure landscape, so called because such enclosures were effected by Act of Parliament. Near the Stockland Hill TV mast in east Devon, this landscape can easily be noticed; the road is wide and so straight that it is thought by some to be Roman. It was in fact made in 1809. The fields are squarish and large, and the new fields destroyed completely one part of an Iron Age hill fort. Near Kentisbeare, when Kentis Moor was enclosed, the same sort of field and landscape was created, and this was commemorated by fixing the horns of the oxen that first ploughed the enclosed fields on a barn wall, and calling the enclosure road Horns Lane. This kind of enclosed landscape, with its large surveyed fields, can be seen in a number of places in the South West, where the upland commons were enclosed and ploughed in the late eighteenth and early nineteenth centuries. Commons had been ploughed in the past but often only temporarily, only as 'outfield', when corn prices were high and the population growing. Now, the old common, rough grazing for all the village cattle, was permanently enclosed and allocated to individuals.

Poverty and hunger created yet another kind of field. Miners could make good use of small plots of land on which to keep a cow and grow potatoes, to supplement their underground wages. In Cornwall much land was parcelled out in small tenements and fields by the miners, and the innumerable small fields at Combe Martin were worked by the silver miners there. On many existing commons the outlines or banks of small plots can be seen, and these were where the hungry poor of the village took in a little piece and tilled it, temporarily, in bad times, as they were allowed to do.

Field names

Whatever their varied origins, all fields have to have names. A farmer needs to tell his wife where he is going to be working, in case a cow calves or the sheep get out or a neighbour calls. He needs also to be able to tell a man where to plough or which hedge to lay without confusion. At Laxton in Nottinghamshire, where open field strips survive to this day, modern contractors have found it difficult to identify the piece of wheat they have been hired to combine. Out of the many adjacent strips growing wheat they have occasionally cut the wrong one. Field names got over any such difficulty.

Field names are difficult to classify and often impossible to explain. To take one farm: Scarswell, in Slapton, South Devon, had, before 1965, twenty-one fields all of them named. Higher and Lower South Parks were south of the farmhouse, the one above the other. Bottom Park was in a valley; Broad Park was wider than long; Long Park was long and narrow; New Park presumably had once been newly created at some uncertain time. Cross Park bordered the old ridge road from Slapton to Stanborough Camp, where perhaps there was at one time a wayside cross.[1] Heathfield, once again at some uncertain date, would have grown heath or heather, as did many local fields. Two farms nearby bear the name. Grange is inexplicable; the word can be used for monastic property but no such association can be found. The 'gratton' in Higher and Lower Gratton means cultivated, ploughed land. Well Park and Well Meadow had springs in them but Well Meadow had a stream running through it. North Park was north of the farmhouse; below it was Calico Meadow, where once, perhaps, calico was bleached on the grass; it was well out of the wind and open. Higher and Lower Common were once presumably unenclosed land, rough scrub claimed by no one originally, but cleared and sown by some energetic past owner. Three Corner explains itself. Great Meadow and New Meadow were hilly fields that had at some time been made into 'catch' water meadows; there was a good stream of water running through the farmyard and there had once been a small dam to feed the contour furrows of the meadows. The name Scarswell means either the spring with water cress, as in Kerswell, or the spring near the Scar, which perhaps meant, aptly in this case, a steep place. Significantly, there are springs breaking out close to the farmhouse.

It will be seen that some sort of history of the use of the land can be constructed from these names, and the same must be true of most farms. However, these names were from the title deeds, and a former owner had quite different names of his own. Furthermore, Slapton has no Tithe Map to authenticate either version. It is possible that a new tenant might make his own names for fields, so there is no guarantee of any antiquity.

Many fields, as at Scarswell, were named after their relationship to the farmhouse, with a Yonder or Homer (near Home) occasionally added to distinguish the relationship a bit further. Fields at the very end of the farm sometimes were nicknamed London or California or some such, merely to emphasize distance.

Names denoting shape explain themselves largely, though the name Strole, is not obvious. It is an access field, often narrow and long, with a way through it to the open moor or to other larger fields. Linch is a terraced field along the side of a hill, often also long and narrow. The terraced footpath on either side of the main road through the village of Sandford near Crediton is the Linch. This is a Saxon word, still in use, and must be related to the more familiar word 'lynchet'. Cleave is steep land, cliff like, and Slade is a flattish valley field. Start is a tail of land, Ball a rounded hill, Gore or Gare a triangular wedge of land, or the site of a fish trap or weir. Field is open land, perhaps not hedged; Hamm is often land near water; Mead is wet meadow and Park implies normally nothing

---

[1] A field in Widecombe with this name was found to have an old cross base buried in the hedgebank.

Plate 1. *Cutting hay near the River Dart.*

Plate 2. *A well-laid and banked West Country hedge. Turf from the field has been used for the bank. 'Browse' remains to be burnt. An unlaid hedge is in the background.*

Plate 3. *A Cornish farming family in 'market' clothes; a hogshead of cider is on the cart.*

Plate 4. *The Parkhouse family outside their farmhouse at Black Torrington, north Devon. The fire-wood faggots in the rick, on the right, will be used in a bread oven or a copper.*

Plate 5. *Devons in the court. Behind is a boarded-up linhay, with a talat for storing hay above.*

Plate 6. *Docile Devons being milked in a north Devon court.*

Plate 7. *Shoeing: a visit to the smithy was a regular event on the farm.*

Plate 8. *Ploughing ley ground with one of the many varieties of 'one-way' plough.*

Plate 9. *Oxen fetching corn: Cornwall c. 1890. The boy is holding an ox goad.*

Plate 10. *Six Devons pulling a wheeled 'zull', the yokes clearly visible. Again this is Cornwall c. 1890, and not a common sight in other parts of England at this time.*

Plate 11. *A hedger with a Devon shovel (its handle cut from the hedge), twobill and cider.*

Plate 12. *A cider press in action, with the cider cheese made from cloths rather than the more traditional straw.*

Plate 13. *'Sacks full, bags full!' Cider apples on the floor of a south Devon orchard. Cider sacks are hanging on the line.*

Plate 14. *Cutting corn with a reaper. The sheaves then had to be made and bound.*

Plate 15. *Making an 'arrish mow' in Cornwall: a small rick built of fifty to sixty sheaves in the corn field. It was one traditional way of saving corn in the damp south-western climate.*

Plate 16. *A threshing machine with reed comber attached; a 'niche' or bundle of reed lies to the left. The men have straw binds in their hands ready to tie the niches.*

Plate 17. *Threshing in the court of Castle an Dinas Farm, Ludgvan, near Penzance in 1939, probably soon after harvest. Heavy sacks of grain are being carried to the corn chamber.*

Plate 18. *A group of harvesters; the teeth of the large arrish rake can just be seen at the men's feet.*

Plate 19. *A family occasion.*

Plate 20. *Haymaking, probably in June. Last winter's supply of mangolds are in a 'cave', still unfinished.*

Plate 21. *Making a hay rick was a social event.*

Plate 22. *Bill King of Landkey, north Devon, by a classic cob and thatch pig house; the little 'tacker' has not been 'breeched' and is perhaps at some risk from the sow.*

Plate 23. *'Fat bacon': farmhouse food for the next few months. The pig on the form has just been slaughtered.*

Plate 24. *'A dog looks up to a man; a cat looks down on a man; a pig looks him straight in the eyes.'*

Plate 25. *Sheep dipping, with a constable in attendance as the law demanded. In the background is a nicely made hipped rick.*

Plate 26. *Family work with a hand-powered shearing machine.*

Plate 27. *Mucking out into a traditional slab-sided wooden barrow.*

Plate 28. *Collecting seaweed, 'ore weed', below the seine-net boats at Mullion, Cornwall.*

Plate 29. *Feeding the chickens: 'wive's business'.*

Plate 30. *A farmer with his flock in a Cornish lane.*

Plate 31. *Women pulling and topping mangolds in Cornwall.*

Plate 32. *Sowing seed from a 'zillup' (seedlip) one-handed.*

Plate 33. *A thatcher holding a 'niche' of reed.*

more remarkable than an enclosed field. However, Deer Park in Hartland, Stoke Fleming and Buckerell, or a Park Farm, as in Combe Martin, refer very probably to medieval deer parks. Duryard, Durpley, and Durley may mean much the same, an animal enclosure or clearing.

Sizes are sometimes referred to. Very small fields were 'quillets' or 'plats'. In Widecombe, one tiny field was called Crowdy. This may be an old Cornish word that has survived somehow, meaning a stable. A horse would be easy to catch in such a small field though no building survives. Nursery field, often close to the farmhouse, may have been for growing on hedge plants or cabbages, but may also have been where lambing ewes were brought for closer attention. A Stitch is often a small field and may be a relic of the open field strips as in 'stitchmeal'. Days Mowth in Widecombe was as big as one man could mow in a day. Not uncommon are small fields with a name such as Old Woman's Acre. Attached to this is often a story about a woman who was granted as much land as she could harvest, dig, or plough in a day. Some small fields are clearly named Forty Acres or Sixty Acres, that could never have been that large. These are farmers' jokes; in Ilsington, one such field was so named so that the owner could go to Newton market and boast that his smallest field was forty acres or that he had finished ploughing or harvesting his 'forty acres'!

Crops once grown in a field occasionally have conferred a name. Flax Park, Hemp Plot, Ryehill and Rye Field must be of this nature, though it is difficult to understand why one year's crop should be thought worth commemorating. Perhaps these crops were unusual, and the farmers were in fact saying 'that field where we once grew flax'. Farmers carried in their memories a calendar of crops and harvests and events from past years. They would remember the date of something happening, a birth, a death, an accident, by referring to the weather, the year of the blizzard, or to 'the year we had the lambing pen in such and such a field', or to some catastrophe, for example, 'the year of the commotion', in that case 1549, the year of the Prayer Book Rebellion.

The condition of a field is also frequently described in the name. 'Arrish' and 'eddish' are words for the stubble of a corn field, while eddish also refers to the aftermath or stubble of a hayfield; these are still in current use, but as field names they make even less sense than the other crop names. Beatland, or the burnt field, refers to the process of beat burning. Brake refers to rough land where bracken – merely 'fern' to a farmer – and brake weed, a small weed of poor soils, grew, and which might be broken to grow a crop. 'Brake' must in fact mean land fit to be broken, though not originally part of the regular cropping land of the farm. Another name with the same meaning is Breachland. Land completely newly enclosed from the common would be a 'newtake'. Furze Park clearly grew furze, though this may well have been grown as a crop and does not necessarily imply waste land. Brimland, and other names like it, probably means land where brambles grew. 'White' in a field name almost certainly refers to wheat or at least to corn, white when it is ripe. 'Black' in the West Country refers to heath or heather and furze, which look black from a distance, and 'green' to good meadow or pasture.

There are a number of functional names. Calico Meadow is perhaps one, and appears in other places as Bleaching Plot. Bleaching linen was a common part of the housewife's work and needed the use of a dry sheltered field from which stock were excluded. Rack Field is almost invariably near a mill, and is where the racks on which cloth was stretched once stood, when the mill was a cloth-making tuck mill or fulling mill. Winnowing Down or often Winding Down was where the corn was winnowed, separated from the chaff by throwing it into the wind, more often than not on the top of a hill. This gave rise to the local expression 'cold as a winnow' cold as a winnower. This is still used, but its significance is forgotten. 'Lears', in contrast, is somewhere well sheltered; a winter lears is where cattle could get in the lew, or have a 'dry bath' as some said. Coldharbour, or names beginning with 'chal' suggest the opposite. Another quite common field name is Butts Park. This must be an old name since it recalls the site of archery butts; practising with the bow was compulsory in every parish in the sixteenth century. There were no less than three of these Butts Parks in Widecombe parish.

Names often make wry comments on fields and their properties. 'Look and Weep' is in fact the name of a cottage near Bovey Heathfield, but Starveall is a field name, as is Costylost, which must mean that the expense in ploughing it or clearing it was lost. Praise seems lacking in field names, though the word Vel as in Velwell, seems to imply deep soil, and Good Fortune may not be just optimistic. Merry is a complimentary word meaning just 'pleasant'. Names like Doggaport ('the dogs' town'), Taddiport, ('the toads' town'), and Beaudiport, ('the horseflies town'), are merely ways of saying that here there were too many of these creatures in those places: 'proper old dogs' town'. Some names do refer to the past. Shilson Field, in Widecombe, refers to a long-gone cromlech of some sort. Old Walls is fairly common but there are seldom any ruins to see any more and Chapel Park may give a clue to a past. Berry, Bury or Barrow almost invariably refer to a ploughed out Bronze Age barrow or hut circle, or some sort of prehistoric bank or earthwork. Some such sites have been first noticed from field names. In Feniton, right beside the railway station, is a market garden called Burland Mead. This may be the site of a barrow known as 'Denebeorg' which was a boundary mark of land granted in a charter to St Mary's Church at Ottery in 1061. Trendle or trundle may have the same sort of meaning as bury; it means a circular round hill or hillock; near Rowtrundle Farm in Roborough is a hut circle. Often the words 'yellow', 'yald', or 'yel' are merely dialect ways of saying 'old' which may refer to land once cultivated but now waste, or land that reveals traces of ancient cultivation. Yellowford in Thorverton is the 'old ford' and Yellowland and Youldon in Holsworthy have the same meaning. These are farm names, but the word is used for fields too. Forches may refer to the site of a gallows; in the last century men were still being hung in chains, often at a parish boundary or on the top of a wild bit of moor.

Sometimes ancient owners' names survive in field names. In Combe Martin are fields recorded in 1840 with the names Tracey and Holland; both these families once owned the manor, but more than 500 years ago. In Slapton there is, or was, a Hawkins Park, but the last member of that famous family to live in Slapton left there nearly 300 years ago. Pressland or Priestland must be pre-Reformation in origin, but Centry or Sentry meaning 'sanctuary' may just refer to church land or glebe land once part of every parish.

Many fields are called after more recent owners or, like Tom's Close, and Cuppier's Piece in Beaford, which may recall the name of the men who cleared and ploughed the ground first. In Combe Martin parish, on Great Hangman, are fields called Witness and Evidence, and there is Witness Moor near Hembury Fort in east Devon. These names perhaps recall some dispute about the boundaries of the parish lands on the open commons. Parishioners perambulated these boundaries regularly at Rogation tide, in order to make sure their rights were not lost. Children were made to learn the boundaries. On Exmoor one old man recalled how, as a boy, he was told by his father not to touch a certain boundstone because it was hot. When he did so, his father rubbed his hand painfully against the stone and said, 'Remember that is a boundstone'.

Some medieval field names may survive. Such are Cain's Acre from the eighth century, the site, presumably, of some quarrel; Pokemead, that is, Puck's mead or goblin's meadow, perhaps echoed in a still surviving Robin's Mead; Murderers' Ash; Hordbury, a site of buried treasure; Wolves' Land, Wolves' Pit, Falconland and prosaically Nepland – turnip land – which comes from as far back as 1292.

Names that derive from the old open fields and their furlongs, are clearly ancient. Landscore, not uncommon as a field name, must describe an open field strip. In 1903 Braunton Great Field was divided into a number of furlongs each with a large number of strips. These were known only by the furlong name. There might be twenty or thirty of these known to their owners, but otherwise indistinguishable. At Brixham were eight furlongs, all divided into plots, all of which took their names from the different furlongs. There were forty-seven plots with the name Rea, and fifteen named Wishings. Any group of strip-like hedged fields with the same name, may in fact be an old furlong, fossilized at some time in the past. Furlong itself as a field name is suggestive of antiquity. But in general Devonshire field names and Cornish ones too, where they are not in the Cornish language, do not give an impression of great age. They suggest fairly recent practice and use, and fit an enclosed landscape. While some of these fields must be ancient, carved directly out of the waste, the old names, with a few exceptions, seem not to have survived and present names do not suggest antiquity.

8.
'Mighty Great Hedges'

THE WEST COUNTRY BANK, OFTEN six foot high and crowned with
a living hedge, is the most obvious feature of 'Damnonian' husbandry.
Marshall wrote: 'the extraordinary fences of this part of the island mark
it most discriminately – common and peculiar to the peninsula – even to
this day.' It was one of his twenty-eight peculiarities. Visitors today exclaim
at the size and growth of the hedges and deplore the consequent loss of
the superb views, of which they can catch a tantalising glimpse, over the
occasional gateway.

Many hedgebanks are six or seven hundred years old, dating from the
time when the medieval landscape was created. There is good evidence
to suggest that some may be prehistoric. Around the edges of Dartmoor
some of the hedgebanks merge with the system of field boundaries, dating
from the bronze age, known as reaves, which suggest an origin of great
antiquity. Certainly Saxon boundary banks survive, and they can be traced
in documentary sources. Part of the estate of Ottery St Mary granted to
the canons of Rouen by Edward the Confessor in 1061 was bounded by
a 'hollow way', a deep lane between two high banks. This is probably
Landscore Lane, still intact as it leads from Fenny Bridges up Gittisham
Hill and still, after nine and a half centuries, marking the boundary of
Ottery St Mary parish. Early charters have regular references to hollow ways,
but in fact almost every lane in Devon, sunk between its high banks, and
sunk most deeply where the bedrock is deep and the run-off of surface water
sharp, is a hollow way. Some banks can be precisely dated. Two largish
fields at Bowrish near Tavistock were divided into three smaller fields each
in 1491 and there were still six fields there in 1969.

Modern ecology and botany have devised a theoretical way of dating a
hedge. In any thirty-yard stretch of hedge there will almost certainly be
quite a number of different woody species of tree or shrub or bush. The
simple rule of thumb is that for every species counted the hedge is a
hundred years old. Clearly the rule must be used discreetly, for example,

some hedges built within the last century were planted with, and still contain, four species. Very often, on the evidence of this technique, the oldest hedges seem to be those nearest to the farmstead and the boundary hedges of both farm and parish. Some huge banks, on the other hand, can be quite new. In 1820 the Knight family bought Exmoor Forest from the Crown and immediately surrounded some 20 000 acres with a purpose-built earth and stone bank some five or more feet high. Some of the bank was planted with nursery grown beech and much of this massive structure, built so it is said, by Irish labourers still survives. Clearly there were still, in 1820, good reasons for building and planting the bank in the south-western fashion, and there are doubtless newer ones on later enclosures of moorland.

One question, asked again and again, relates to the reasons for and the origin of these great banks. There are obvious answers but all are only partial. The first is to do with the South West's exposure to westerly gales. These winds are rarely bitterly cold, but they are almost always wet, and their chill factor is increased by their strength. Wet cold gales are hard on stock, particularly young stock, and a good bank provides a wonderful 'lew', or in sailor's terms a 'lee', out of the wind. In such winds most stock make for the 'lew' of the hedge and turn their tails to the wind, or bed down on a dry patch. Sheep occasionally need to be driven into such shelter and farmers spread hay and straw in the shelter of the hedge. Removing a hedge alters the micro-climate, reduces the temperature of the soil by a fraction and may delay spring growth a trifle. This argument, for shelter as the principal reason for the hedgebank, is not totally convincing; stock could be housed, though it would be expensive; a well grown thorn hedge planted on a low bank or on the natural surface of the land would do the job nearly as well. There must be parts of the country, equally windy, where stock were not normally housed in winter that lack the hedgebank completely. Nevertheless in winter a hedgebank does serve a useful purpose in providing shelter, so it must be part of the explanation.

Secondly, hedges provide timber of all sorts: firewood, faggots, and useful timber trees if saplings are left to grow. Where there was no coal, no peat and no moorland to cut 'vags' and little woodland, or the woodland was reserved by the landlord, hedges provided the only means of heating the house. Their timber was carefully preserved. Covenants in leases forbade cutting more than once in so many years and stipulated that so many saplings should be left to grow. Hedges, in fact, provided a crop to exploit but also to conserve: 'an overplus of poles, cordwood, faggots and the bark of oak, for sale'. But again this explanation is only partially satisfactory. Most of England lacked such hedgebanks but kept itself warm from the coppicing of woodland; it is not clear why this could not be done in the South West, unless there was little woodland to exploit. This was, in fact, Marshall's explanation.

Thirdly, small, hedged fields certainly made the best use of grass, and stock could be shifted regularly to advantage, as indicated by Hooker as early as 1600. However, to do this did not require the building of the massive hedgebanks. Perhaps all these reasons put together are sufficient explanation, but banks remain something of an enigma.

Their construction presents certain problems too. They contain massive amounts of earth or stone which had to be dug from somewhere, yet the banks are not matched or fronted by a ditch from which the material might have come. It is possible that there once was a ditch before every bank, which has filled in over the passage of the centuries and the making and the remarking of the bank, but there is little trace of them. Where the soil is heavy and the water has to be carried off, there is often a ditch, but in no way big enough to provide the material to build the bank. Marshall thought they had grown in bulk with time and constant rebuilding, and concluded their age was 'great beyond memory'.

It is possible that the banks are what remains of original woodland, that a field was cleared as far as the line of the present hedge and that there the natural growth was left to grow untouched, and that around its base earth was piled up to make a stock-proof bank which has merely been added to over the centuries. Some field banks are well colonized by dog's mercury (*Mercurialis perennis*). This is a shade-loving woodland plant that spreads only vegetatively, a few inches a year, not setting seed. It seems to follow that if specimens of this plant flourish and survive on a bank or hedge, then that bank was once woodland, however far away any existing woods may now be.

Yet another possibility is that these banks contain the remains of clearing the land, the old roots, boulders, tree stumps, even tree trunks, that had to be removed before the land could be ploughed. These could have been piled up in rows to form the base of a hedge. But surface stone, except on Dartmoor and the Cornish moors, is not so prevalent as to provide enough material for all these lowland banks. Some banks are quite clearly stone filled and can only have been constructed with stone from a local quarry, and this may be how many were built. The labour was immense. Working from about November to March most days of the week it took two men to rebuild about a quarter of a mile of a badly 'roozed down' bank on both sides, cut the hedge timber, lay the hedge and faggot the brush wood. It took the Knights five years, between 1820 and 1824, to build twenty-nine miles of the boundary bank of Exmoor, using possibly up to 200 Irish labourers.

Hedgebanks, while traditionally acceptable and useful, are often anathema to the incomer. They have obvious disadvantages, one being that they occupy a lot of land. One calculation has suggested that one seventh of a farm of 100 acres, where the average size of the fields was four acres, that is fourteen acres or so, was occupied by hedgebanks. Further, when the hedge is ten years old or more, it shades the grass and drips on any crops. By one reckoning a strip of land twenty-five feet in width was 'waste' because of the bank itself and the shade it cast. Banks hinder drying winds and can provide miles of interconnecting luxurious dry warm burrows for rabbits, a gold mine for the rabbit trapper, but a creeping destructive pest to the farmer unless he was one of those who paid the rent with rabbits. (In the 1920s and 30s many did just that!)

Nor are hedgebanks, unless very well maintained, an 'insuperable barrier to stock'. Allowing the hedge timber to grow created gaps in the hedge eventually, and in April and May young lambs like nothing better than playing 'Follow my leader' and 'I'm the king of the castle' over and around the hedge. Once one lamb has found its way inadvertently into the next field, it will surely be unable to get back, and before long one ewe, and then all the ewes, will be over on the principle that the grass really is greener in someone else's field.

In spite of all these snags the banks remain, and few farmers destroy them completely though many miles must have gone since the Second World War. Today few cut the hedge growth for timber; instead, a hedge trimmer creates an almost impenetrable hedge along the top of the bank by yearly pruning. One shoot is cut back to form two and the result is a mass of growth more or less impervious to stock, and the bank remains intact. It still provides valuable shelter, and where banks have been removed, farmers find they need to plant windbreaks of ugly conifers, often very slow to grow and pretty well useless for firewood.

In the past hedges were cut and laid, and banks made up at least every ten to twelve years. It was in theory always done the year a field was ploughed. There were good reasons for this. Firstly, an unlaid hedge would shade the corn crop, causing it to ripen unevenly and 'lodge' or 'go lie', that is, break and bend over just above ground level to form a green unripe mass, difficult to cut with a reaphook or a binder. Much of the grain was lost like this or eaten by mice or other vermin. Secondly, if any crop needed to be protected from stock it was the corn crop. Boy Blue had to blow on his horn to get the cows out of the corn not merely because the crop would suffer, but because cows do not know where to stop and would 'blow' on too much lush green growth or unripe grain, and die all too easily. Hence the need for a well maintained, stock-proof hedge around a newly ploughed field. Thirdly, making up the bank requires plenty of growing turf and quantities of earth to fill the holes and face the bank. This can most easily be got from the sward and earth of the adjoining grass field. Pairing off the grass for facing the bank would leave bare patches in the sward, but this is of no consequence if the field is then ploughed.

The ideal hedgebank was not far from the vertical, and without breaks in the surface on which sheep could find a foothold. The soil had to be firm and well solidified, much easier on heavier soils. The hedge, ideally, consisted of a continuous gapless layer of almost horizontal growing stems of thorn, nut or withy. This layer had to be thick enough to be a deterrent to stock, consisting of at least four stems, each no more than a couple of inches thick and at least a foot high, all of this surmounting and slightly overhanging the bank. These 'hedders', or 'edders' or 'hethers' needed to be 'quick', alive and growing, so that they put on leaf in spring to make the hedge that much more impenetrable. They were kept in place by crooks, inverted Vs of wood cut from the hedge with one long leg, driven deep into the bank. The hedge was trimmed to look tidy, and every so often oak, ash, elm, holly or beech saplings were left to grow into timber trees. To achieve this ideal was not easy. A hedger first needed good, sharp tools:

a bill hook for cutting the thinner wood; an axe and saw for the heavier timber; a long-handled Devon shovel to earth and turf up the high bank; a twobill or bizzard for cutting roots and paring away the collapsed earth of the bank (fig. 23). This was like a pickaxe but with one point edged like an axe for cutting roots and the other flat like a mattock for the digging work. Also needed were a staff hook – a blade on a long handle for cutting and trimming branches out of ordinary reach – and a pair of hedger's gloves to protect the hands from the spikes of blackthorn that so often festered in the skin.

Faced with an overgrown hedge and a largely collapsed bank, the first task was to cut off all the larger timber from the hedge that was not needed for 'heddering', that is, making the final hedge. This had to be done just so, the cut clean and vertical. Ragged stubs provoked the remark 'well, I suppose a blind man would like to see it!' The stubs of the timber would continue to grow, providing upward growing shoots for the next cutting of the hedge in ten years time or so. If they were cut flat they gathered water in the bole, which caused them to rot and die.

The poles from this cutting were then piled up to be taken to the farmyard and built into upright pyramids that would dry out. The smaller branches and twigs and shoots would be cut off to be made into faggots. The bigger timber was useful for the handles of tools. Holly was normally left to grow, but where it was cut it was the best wood for the beating part of a flail. Ash, a flexible wood, was good for the ladders at each end of a cart or wagon that supported the loads of hay or corn. Elm was best for any damp or wet use, and the straight branches of hazel and withy were sawn into lengths of about three feet, and then split longitudinally into three or four with a small fine spar hook to make thatcher's spars, vital for fixing the thatching ropes to the rick. Men were always on the look-out for the right shaped piece for an axe handle or, most difficult of all, the long curved handle of a Devon shovel (plate 11). These were hard to find, and it was always said that if one was found growing it should be cut immediately there and then, since finding it again in the mass of the hedge was impossible.

Firewood varied and the properties of each wood were well known. Ash was and, of course, still is the very best; like no other wood it burns brightly wet, green or dry, and out of it the Christmas faggot was made.

> Ash wet or ash dry
> A queen can warm her slippers by.

Oak burnt slowly and gave great heat, but needed to be dead dry. Elm smouldered and glowed, seldom in flames; beech burnt quickly, and of course pine or fir spat sparks dangerously.

Faggots were necessary to start any fire and vital to boil up hot water in the kitchen 'copper'. An inexhaustible supply was needed by a busy housewife. Faggots were made by laying a long thin piece of withy or nut, a 'bind', flat on the ground. The brush was then cut to a length and piled up in a great bundle on the withy 'bind'. When the bundle was big enough the bind was pulled absolutely tight round the faggot and tied in a kind of knot by twisting and doubling back both ends around each other and pushing the ends into the mass of the faggot to fix them. This needed strong hands. Making faggots caused a lot of banter: if they were too small, the 'crows could carry them away'; if too big they could not be lifted by pitch fork or 'pick' on to the top of a rick or a load by one man, as they had to be. The worst thing was to make a faggot that fell apart. Once finished they were built into a rick of faggots in the farmyard close to the house, shaped just like a corn rick with a sloping roof, though unthatched. Faggots were also useful for putting underneath stacks of corn or hay to raise the rick off the damp earth. It was no good using this year's faggots for firing, they had to dry for a year, so there were often two or three ricks of these in and around the farmyard.

Having dealt with the faggots and poles, the next thing was to face up the bank. For this the long Devon shovel was vital; very little of what follows could have been done without its long reach. The first thing to do was to pare back the earth of the collapsed bottom of the hedge with the twobill, until there was a nearly vertical surface along the proper line of the bottom of the hedge. This earth was then piled up into any hollow places in the bank, using the shovel for this and tamping it all into place with the back of the blade, 'six inches off the bottom, six inches on the top'. Using the shovel again, a flat ledge, two or three inches deep, was dug into this face and on to this a layer of growing turves was placed and again tamped into the earth, so that they would root and grow. This turf was sliced from the surface of the field, again with the shovel. If the hedge was a boundary between two farms, a man doing up both sides of the hedge was allowed to use six feet of the turf in his neighbour's field for this purpose. Once one layer of turf was in place, more earth was heaped up behind and tamped down, and another layer of turf put in place on the top of the first, and so on until the top of the bank was reached. The angle of the bank had to be calculated rightly, not too steep for the turves to keep in place securely, but not too shallow, or sheep and lambs would clamber up and bring everything down. A man had to have in his mind's eye the exact, nearly upright line of the bank from top to bottom, and make his work conform to this and to the existing line of the hedge. It was not easy. A big bank was often eight to ten feet wide at the base, six feet or more high, narrowing to five feet or so at the top. Once built, a bank was expected to stay up for some years despite the interference of stock. The heavier the soil the easier this was to do. The whole business was laborious and in later times farmers would plough out the bottom of a bank where it had collapsed, and shovel this quickly back into place. This was better than nothing.

The job was not yet finished. Once the bank was built the next thing was to make the actual hedge with the hedders left in place initially. These were cut partly through, about two thirds was about right, near their base, and bent over more or less horizontally. Once again the cut had to be clean and tidy; rain water from the hedder should not run down into the cut to cause it to rot, since it was from there again that the necessary new growth came. It was easy to cut too strongly and sever the hedder and leave too few hedders to make a hedge; dead wood could be left, or a bit of thorn stuffed in, but this was then not a growing hedge. The brush end of the hedder was then secured by crooks with the shorter leg of the crook over the stem of the hedder and the longer leg driven deep into the hedge. Loose earth was then shovelled upon to the top surface of the hedge to encourage rooting and new growth. To finish the job, the brush ends of the hedders were pared off with a sharp staff hook to look tidy. The ideal hedge had been created, something of a work of art, tidy and stock proof, to look at with pride and satisfaction (plate 2).

On Dartmoor, stone walls took the place of hedgebanks, though they were sometimes filled out with earth, or built with an earth core to form something like the more conventional bank. The process of walling and banking was presumably simultaneous with clearing the fields of the moorstone that could be moved, so as to make ploughing or cultivation easier. Similar stone walls exist around the Cornish moors and wherever there was stone to be picked up without too much difficulty. To make a really good firm stone wall that would deter moorland sheep and cattle was highly skilled, but the skill is difficult to describe. A good waller, it was said never put down a stone once he had picked one up, the one in the hands would always fit: such was the experience and skill and eye of the craftsman. One technique was to use 'through' stones, big heavy stones that fitted right across the thickness of the wall, to give stability to the two faces that tended to slip apart with frost and rain and disturbance. Another was to place large stones on the very top layer, as least likely to be dislodged by an animal. Good walls had a row of upright stones in the middle of the top surface to make a foothold hard to find. Farm labourers were expected to be able to wall, along with their many other skills.

On Dartmoor some enormous stones, that would take many men to move them, form part of a wall. With this task, as with hedging, there were times of the year when there was little other seasonal work on the farm, and it was necessary to keep the men busy, labour being, after all, normally cheap. Probably there has hardly ever been a time when labour on the farm was not cheap for what it did. Between 1596 and 1796 in Devon, labourer's wages rose by a half, but the cost of living rose three times, and much the same can be said for the next century or so until more modern times. One apt monument to the generations and generations of labourers that are otherwise unremembered might be the miles and miles of hedgebank and wall that they built and maintained with little reward. No part of the South West is without such a reminder.

9.
Ploughing and Tilling

HAVING MADE UP THE BANKS and laid the hedges, a man had to plough. Ploughing a well-grazed, well-trodden, grass sward was difficult with the old ploughs. The turf had a tough spine and was hard to bury and unless it was buried it would 'show green' and start to grow again, and make the proper tilling of corn impossible. It was likely also, after seven or eight years in grass, that 'stroil' or couch grass had taken over. This was a persistent and invasive grass weed that would 'destroy all', hence its south-western name. To Slapton men it was known as 'Blackawton clover' as being the best in their view that Blackawton, with its poor weedy land, could manage in the way of a good sward. It had to be destroyed, but ploughing did not kill it. It could be ripped up and burnt after harvest, or another way was to burn the whole surface of the field all as a preliminary to ploughing. This left no turf to bury and cleaned the field of weeds.

This process was known as 'Devonshiring' or 'beat burning' and seems to have originated in Devon or at least in the South West. It is easy to see why. Grass grew abundantly in the warm damp climate, and farmers practiced ley farming or alternate husbandry, which alternated corn crops with grass regularly. They had to find a means to plough grassland efficiently. In much of the rest of England grass was rarely ploughed and arable remained arable with only the fallow as a break. Beat burning had no place in that system, but in the South West where grass often got overgrown and there was much rough land to plough and till, it had a vital part to play.

'Devonshiring', or 'beat burning'

Devonshiring was a complicated and laborious process. First the top two or three inches of the sward had to be pared off. This could be done by hand, using a beat axe. This was thought to be the hardest work on the farm. Hacking away at the surface of the field with a broad-bladed mattock and slicing off the turf gave the impression that men were actually beating the soil (fig. 23). This may explain one name for the process. Fitzherbert knew of the practice and wrote that 'they must go beat their lands as they do in Devon and Cornwall'. Hand beating was much used in Cornwall in Colepresse's day; it was practical where very rough stony land, full of roots of furze or heather, was being prepared for ploughing. In later years the beat axe was essentially a tool of small farmers.

It was quicker, but not much less laborious, to pare off the turf by using either a breast plough or a paring shovel. The first was pushed by a man using his chest and arms. It was fitted with an upturned sharp edge to the mouldboard that cut off the turf in a continuous slice. It, was also a small farmer's tool, enabling a man who could not afford a yoke of oxen to pare and plough laboriously (fig. 24). The paring shovel was much like the ordinary Devon 'ace of spades' shovel except that it had an upturned edge to cut turf, and also a flattened handle to enable turves of a good length to be sliced off. This shovel was often used for cutting 'vags or turves' for 'firing' on moory ground.

Quickest of all was to use an ordinary 'zull' or plough, fitted with a 'velling' share (fig. 25). This cut a thin plough slice which was no less than fourteen inches wide compared to the normal seven or eight. It had a coulter and an upturned wing to cut the slice cleanly both sides. This would have been used on easily ploughed grass fields where there were no rocks or roots. It was with this velling share that 'skirting' was practised. Skirting involved inverting the plough slice on to unploughed grass so that grass was laid on top of grass. Deprived of light and air these two grassy turves rotted quickly and could then be easily broken up with harrows and burnt. This was also known as combing or ribbing since it produced on the field surface a regular raised pattern like the teeth of a comb, or the ribs of a boat or a body. This was sometimes then ploughed again across the original line of ploughing to free the rotted turf completely, a process known as 'thwarting' (going athwart).

Once pared off in these ways the turf or beat was left to dry. Beat burning began in May in order to catch the driest weather, and the beat was ready to be 'twitched', turned over by hand, in a few days of heat. It was then broken up into small pieces by harrowing it at the trot with toothed drag harrows. The harder it was hit with the harrow the easier it would break up. This was 'beat trotting' done with two horses to the harrow with a boy mounted on one to urge them on to greater speed. Farm boys probably loved that job. Small farmers got their wives and children to break up the pared turves by hand. When really dry the beat was raked together into heaps. This was done with a beat rake, a hay rake only with narrower set teeth, or by using a 'drudge', a heavy solid beam of wood, pulled by a horse cross-wise. When iron chain harrows were used, the beat would collect in the mesh of the harrow, until there was too big an accumulation to stay put. This then freed itself into a large heap for burning.

Once heaped into burrows and shaken up to let the air in, the beat was set alight with a handful of straw and encouraged to burn till it was all

Fig. 24. Breast plough: pushed with
the full weight of the body for
stripping off turf prior to beat burning
or Devonshiring

Fig. 25. Broad 'velling'
share, for slicing off the
first inches of turf before
beat burning

Fig. 26. The tormentor or
spurtang: for ripping up
hard arable ground

consumed. Worgan writes that when this was going on in Cornwall the whole countryside was enveloped in smoke. It was this too that made it impossible in Marshall's view to distinguish a village of unplastered cob cottages with smoking chimneys, from a burning beat field. Once burnt, the ashes of the beat were mixed with manures and spread on the field.

This was the far-famed 'Devonshiring'. Colepresee said that it was 'so termed in Kent and other counties for its long and continued practice in the county'. It was certainly an ancient practice, the Latin word for it in medieval documents was *baticium*. It was being done both by hand and with a plough as early as 1246 at Tavistock, and at Slapton by 1307 by tenant farmers, as a service in lieu of rent. At Hurdwick near Tavistock it took a day to burn half an acre in this way. All later observers of south-western farming remarked on it, and it was still being practised well into this century. The late Mr Hermon French of Widecombe in the Moor himself 'trotted' beat as a boy, and could remember a neighbour beat burning between the wars. But he gave it up because it was so laborious and needed a long period of fine dry weather. Ploughs with velling shares were, however, still known near Holsworthy in the 1950s.

Whether the practice really originated in Devon is uncertain. All the early writers thought so, but they may have been copying each other. Chapple believed it was once much more used because it was the only way to reclaim the vast amount of moory waste in the county. Marshall thought Devon and Cornwall were the 'fount and source' of the practice, and listed it among his twenty-eight peculiarities. It was later practised all over England, but was commonly known as paring and burning, and was thought useful for taking in rough grassland and moor.

As to its value, opinions were divided. The Duke of Bedford forbade it in many of his leases on his Tavistock estates and could not, as a consequence, get enough tenants to rent his farms. Marshall knew farmers of good status and knowledge who failed because they were not allowed to burn beat. He himself had grave doubts about it, but pointed out that arable land was remarkably free of weeds after beat burning, and that farms otherwise not well managed fetched as high rents in the South West as in better farmed counties, and that the state of husbandry could not be as good as it was if it was really harmful. Local opinion was that it in some way stimulated fertility, and that liming was less necessary after a field had been burnt.

The obvious objection to burning was that when the turf was burnt the organic matter, the humus, would be destroyed. This loss could be made up to some extent by the application of manures, and from an early date Devonshiring was almost invariably accompanied by heavy dressings of dung, lime, sea sand or marl. At Milton Abbot, in 1246, only so much land was allowed to be burnt as could be dressed with manure, and later leases stipulated heavy dressings, thirty tons of dung and two tons of lime, to accompany burning. It was common practice to mix the ashes with lime or sand and all the local road scrapings, pile it all in a heap to mature and then 'scode' it, spread it all over the field and plough it in. After that no

Fig 27. *Devon 'one-way' plough or zull. This one had two hinged mouldboards (a). Tilted appropriately, it could plough to left or right, thus always casting the furrow uphill when contour ploughing. The angle of the coulter (b) could also be adjusted.*

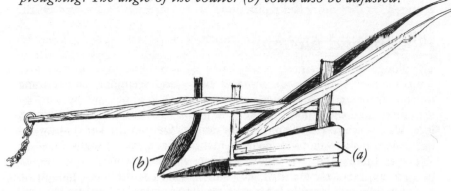

Fig. 28. *Drag harrows; made in two sections to conform to the shape of a narrow plough ridge.*

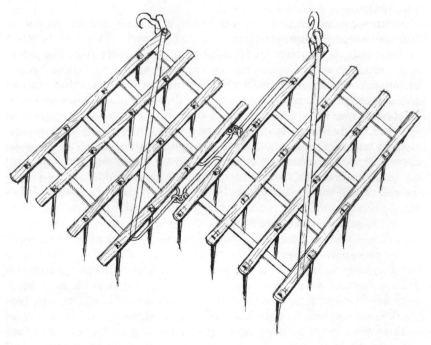

further manures were thought necessary for the following crops. It does seem as if Devonshiring was viewed by many farmers as a vital and necessary preliminary to all crops. It became a sort of panacea with an almost magical reputation for enhancing fertility, and was probably used to excess and thus acquired, in the end, a bad reputation.

Ploughs and ploughing

The plough used by farmers in the South West was known as the zull (and sometimes the sewl or sole). It was a heavy and seemingly cumbersome instrument made by any hedge carpenter out of local oak and apple. The iron shares and the coulter that cut the ground could be fashioned by the local blacksmith to each farmer's own design. Only in the last century did implement makers set up in towns to make the new iron ploughs.

The zull looked clumsy, but Vancouver thought it worked well 'despite its rude appearance'. Marshall, however, thought it the worst plough he had seen, and said it reminded him of ploughs painted by heraldic painters, or pictured on pub signs. He thought these pictures showed 'Norman' ploughs, and concluded that the design of the 'zull' had not changed for eight hundred years! He considered that it ploughed grass satisfactorily but made only a mark in arable land. It had a long mouldboard that on grass land 'whelmed the furrow completely over' and it could be fitted with a variety of shares to cut a furrow. Marshall also saw a special paring plough with a fourteen inch share to prepare the land for beat burning that 'performed its business very well'.

Another plough common in the South West, but rare in the rest of England was the 'turn wrest' or 'one-way' plough. This was designed to cope with the problem of ploughing steep hill sides (fig. 27). These were ploughed as part of the normal rotation of grass and corn. Neither horses nor oxen could normally plough up steep hillsides. After years of ordinary ploughing and cultivation down hill, much of the soil would have descended by gravity to the bottom of the hill, leaving the top of the field very thin. To avoid this, farmers ploughed their furrows along the contours. Ploughs normally turn the furrow to the right only. Going across the slope in one direction an ordinary plough would throw the furrow satisfactorily up hill but, returning in the other direction, the furrow would be thrown down the hill, which was unsatisfactory. In the South West, therefore, a plough was designed so that the furrow could be thrown either to left or right as needed. The ploughman could simply shift the mouldboard at the end or each furrow and turn the soil up hill every time, thus the term 'one-way'. Such a plough was known to Fitzherbert in Kent, but the only other known home of such an ingenious device is the South West. However, Colepresse did not know of such a plough in Devon and Cornwall in his day (1667), since he describes how ploughs had to 'wind about lairy', that is, pull the plough up hill 'empty', not ploughing, probably on its side. All sorts of what were called, confusingly, one-way ploughs were designed and constructed of iron in the South West, during the last century. This shows a great interest by farmers in preventing erosion and loss of soil. Some steep terrace-like fields could only have been ploughed along the contours in this way, but others from their shape must always have been ploughed up and down. To get over this some farmers used a great horse drawn scoop or shovel to get soil back up the hill. This worked very well until the blade of the scoop hit an obstacle and threw the driver on his nose over the scoop behind the horses feet!

On flatter land ploughing could be done conventionally enough, marking a field out into 'lands' and ploughing 'up' one side and 'down' the other, turning each plough furrow towards a ridge in the middle. The first furrow had to be cut absolutely straight; nothing was worse than a bit of ploughing that looked like a dog's hind leg. Neighbours would be sure to see it and there would be wry comments in the pub or at market. So markers had to be put in each hedge and both ploughman, who held the plough, and ploughboy, who led the ploughteam, had to keep the plough dead in line. Ploughmen took great pride in making a straight even furrow. For a labourer, pride in work done was one of the few satisfactions in an otherwise ill-paid, poorly regarded, and poorly housed job. It was a skill to be cultivated and time was allowed for it. There were chances to match skills and teams and implements at ploughing matches, with horses groomed to a shine and decked out with brasses and cockades in all their finery.

Farmers were fussy about how ploughing was done. One necessity for growing a good crop, before the fertilizer bag made it easy, was to get a good tilth, not too loose or 'plum', or too hard for the seed to germinate. It was a matter of instinctive judgement; many farmers who could grow fine malting barley could not explain how they did it, they just knew. So they would drag the toes of their boots in the soil here and there and pronounce judgement on the day's ploughing or cultivating. They could be pernickety. 'Well, Jack, you'm doing a master job, but I fancy us wants to go a barley corn deeper'. A barley corn was an eighth of an inch! If the land was too plum it needed rolling, too hard it needed a stroke of the tormentor or, in South Hams parlance, the spurtang (fig. 26). 'The farmers foot' was 'the best manure'.

Before the days of tractor cabs ploughing was an agreeable job. If the plough is set right and the soil in the right condition, the turning of the furrow is a delight to watch as the yellow of the arrish or the green of grass twists into the brown or red of ploughed earth. If the mould board is shiny and polished, kept rust free with grease and the soil just damp, the turning furrow will 'sing' as it turns and will have a shine to it where the clay particles are polished by the mould board. Ploughing was always accompanied by a great flutter and screech of gulls as they battled for worms and grubs, a whirl of white and grey, brown and black.

Ploughing seems always to have been a source of pleasure, though the labour of walking up to sixteen miles a day behind the plough, and hanging on hard to the handles for seven back-and-shoulder-twisting hours, was immense. Marshall gives a delightful account of the way a man and boy worked with an ox team: the boy singing to the oxen, dropping and raising his note an octave at intervals, while the ploughman directed the oxen in a gruffer voice.

The style of driving cannot pass unnoticed by a stranger. The language, though peculiar to the country, does not arrest the attention, but the tone or tune in which it is delivered resembles with great exactness the chantings and recitative of the Cathedral service. The plough boy chants the counter tenor with unabated ardour through the day, the plowman throwing in at intervals his hoarser note. This chanting march, which sometimes may be heard to a considerable distance, encourages and animates the team as the music of a marching army or the song of the rowers. I have never seen so much cheerfulness attending the operation of ploughing anywhere as in Devonshire.

Vancouver added that when the chanting stopped the oxen stopped too! Baring-Gould collected a song called 'The Oxen Ploughing' which may reflect some of this delight and pleasure, though it only faintly suggests the ploughboy's tune.

> Prithee lend your vocal voices,
> For to listen we're agreed,
> Come sing of songs the choicest,
> Of the life the plough boys lead,
> There is none that lives so merry,
> As the ploughboy does in Spring,
> When he hears the sweet birds whistle,
> And the nightingales to sing,
> > *With my hump along! Jump along!,*
> > *Here drives my lad along!,*
> > *Pretty Sparkle Berry, (me quo)*
> > *Good luck Speedwell Cherry, (nice quo)*
> > *We are the lads that can follow the plough.*

Perhaps only the chorus with the names of the oxen and the odd interjections convey anything of the ploughboy's chant. Baring-Gould collected this largely forgotten song at Trebartha in Cornwall from an old man cutting bracken, and memorized words and music riding back the eighteen miles to Lew Trenchard.

Horses or oxen

Baring-Gould never saw oxen ploughing in his life in Devon, but Marshall and Vancouver and Worgan saw them used for both plough and cart. In Cornwall boys liked to trot two oxen to a cart through the streets. The use of oxen seems largely to have died out by the middle of the last century, although there were people still living in Payhembury around 1914, who had once ploughed the flat land inside Hembury Fort with oxen. In Marshall's time the four-ox team was the rule, the oxen were excellent and the ploughmen, who were expert, had no wish to change.

The debate about which was best for work was centuries old, a real pub argument. Oxen, when working, needed good pasture at night, horses were content with rough ground. Oxen would plough up hill and in tough clay, where horses would stand still. Oxen ploughed slower than a man walked, horses were faster. Horses needed hay and corn in winter, oxen just straw. Horse harness was far more expensive than an ox yoke and chain. Oxen were docile, could be quickly trained to the plough, horses need much breaking in. Oxen could work without shoeing, though they did better with ox cues, on the front feet, one to each half off the cloven hoof (figs 33, 34). At the end, if a horse got sick or old, it was 'but carrion', while a fatted ox was 'man's meat'. Fitzherbert's verdict went to the ox.

Oxen pulled sledges, untippable on steep hillsides, and carts, but were not used with a pack-saddle (figs 29, 30). This was, (fig. 31) in the old days, the ordinary means of carriage on the farm; indeed, in Marshall's day there was 'scarce a pair of wheels in the country, at least not on a farm'. A special breed of packhorse had been developed that was small and light but not much use in a plough, and the big plough horse, the Shire, was little known in the South West at the beginning of the last century. In contrast, the huge South Devon breed of cattle were excellent plough beasts, so there was little impulse to change.

But oxen were slow, despite Marshall's favourable comparison of their pace with that of 'Kentish high fed horse team'. In Cornwall, it was said that two horses could plough an acre a day, whereas four oxen could only manage three-quarters. The ox team needed a man and a boy to work it, whereas new horse-drawn iron ploughs had been invented that could be managed by one man using whip reins. This, and the increasing pace of life ('hurry-push' was the word), ended the ox's long reign as a plough beast, and the old ploughing chorus was heard no more.

Manures and dressings

Before sowing, the land had to be dressed. All the manures used in the old days – sand, lime, dung, marl, and ashes – were bulky and heavy. With few carts and waggons all of these had to be hauled out on the back of a packhorse. For heavy bulky material the pack-saddle was fitted with dung pots, open baskets slung on each side with bottoms that opened, enabling loads to be dumped easily (fig. 31). One such load constituted one 'seame', the common, easily recognizable, south western measure.

Dung

Dung came in all sorts, town night-soil, the contents of the privy, known vulgarly as 'bum dung' and farmyard muck. Many felt instinctively that 'muck was best'. 'Muck is the mother of the meal tub', was a Cornish saying. There was never enough muck and leases forbade its sale off the farm. Farmers made up for this lack sometimes by spreading straw on the roads nearby to mix with the droppings of passing animals. This was then scraped up, mixed with lime or sand, and spread. This may partly account for the enormous depth of some country lanes, well below field level. Short corn-stubble straw was best for bedding cattle sheds, as it made forking it out so much easier. Bracken was put to good use as bedding too, or for roofing a pig's hovel. Leases stipulated the application of 'well rotted dung before ploughing'. This made a good compost, or 'compass' as Tusser called it, mixed with hedge trimmings, lime and sand, left in a great heap in the field to mature. Then it was taken out into small heaps and spread. Village boys would spread the heaps for pocket money, and then it was ploughed in as quickly as possible before it lost its goodness. Some men wisely built sheds to keep the rain off the dung heap.

Everything went on to the muck heap, including dead pigs, calves and lambs; once covered up they rotted quickly. The parish registers of Hemyock even record in 1647 that the body of a girl who died of the plague was 'laid up in dung', perhaps to avoid a journey through a plague stricken village to the churchyard. In this century, one old man, driven half out off his mind with debt, put his own wife's body on the muck heap, perhaps to avoid funeral expenses. In a rough-and-ready society these are not likely to be the only times this happened.

Other sources of organic manures were seaweed and waste fish, known in Cornwall as 'caff'. Some curious beliefs surrounded these fertilizers; it was thought that corn grown with seaweed was useless as seed, and that the fertilizing effect on the land lasted a year only. One rotten pilchard, it was believed, would manure a large area of ground. Waste salt and the oozings of oil from pilchard barrelling were also used. Farmers near the sea would make good use of these manures and for those near towns, woollen and brewing wastes were sometimes available. Nothing organic was wasted.

Muck was usually considered the best, but by itself it was not enough. It feeds the soil with plant foods, but does nothing to alter acidity, to sweeten the naturally acid soils of much of the South West. Oats and rye will stand some acidity, but no farmer could grow wheat or barley on really acid land, so something else was needed. Leases of farms stipulated that either dung, or lime, or sand should be applied to land, but these are not substitutes, and farmers learnt this from an early date.

Sea sand

In Cornwall farmers relied almost entirely on sea sand to sweeten their soils. Nowhere in Cornwall is very far from the sea or an estuary, and sand was packhorsed from beaches or from river barges. Latterly the Bude Canal (built in 1826) took sand many miles inland. Sand from north Cornwall was largely broken shell, and was almost wholly calcium carbonate. There were said to be thirty-four different sorts; the best came from Mother Ivey Bay, Constantine Bay and Gwithian Dunes; these are between seventy-five and eighty per cent calcium carbonate. Sand dug from banks exposed by the tide contained less shell but some organic matter, in particular a slime known as 'liggan' in Cornwall, said to be excellent for potatoes. Beach sand was mainly just shell, and both types of sand reduced acidity and lightened heavy soils.

Cornishmen have a charter from King Henry III allowing them to take sand freely from the beaches, though of course they had to pay for carriage. Devon men had no such charter and had presumably to pay for sand to the landowner. The monks of Tavistock kept a string of packhorses working all summer, fetching sand from Widemouth Bay; but they had to pay tolls to the local lord for the privilege. They used this sand at Werrington, fourteen miles from the sea. It was hard work for the horses, so much so that it is recorded in 1350 the 'no foals were born by reason of great toil in fetching sand'.

In Devon, in the eighteenth century, sand was used in all parishes within reach of the sea on the north and south coasts, (east Devon excepted), and within reach also of the numerous estuaries, particularly the Tamar. Not all the sand was of good quality, but most farmers had probably only their observation of effects with which to make a judgement. By the seventeenth century some said that lime answered better than sand. This could only be so if sand low in calcium was being used. Some farming practices became crazes, used without thought as a sort of universal panacea. Marl and beat burning were used in this way and it may also be true of sand.

Unless a man had his own horses, he would employ a carrier with a packhorse train to fetch sand as needed. Near the sea, sand was spread at 200 sacks per acre but inland sixty sacks was more common, spread by hand from a 'zillup'. Some land, Colepresse says, was glutted with sand, but in general sand, along with lime, enabled farmers to grow wheat and barley and other crops where they could not do so before and also to increase existing yields. The first person to comment on Devon farming, William of Malmesbury, writing c. 1100, said that Devon soils were so poor that they only grew oats. Without some 'sweetening' agent they could do little else, so it is possible that the use of sand, from at least 1250, and marl in east Devon also from medieval times, revolutionized cereal growing in the South West. At Tavistock, wheat only began to supplement oats in the fourteenth century.

Lime

By the eighteenth century there were probably few places in Devon out of reach of a lime kiln. Wherever there was a beach or an estuary there were kilns, burning lime from South Wales, Berry Head or Plymouth. There were kilns on open beaches such as at Heddon's Mouth, Slapton and Buck's Mills. Wherever there was limestone quarry inland – such as at Burlescombe, Ashburton, and Chudleigh – there were kilns also.

Limestone was quarried and brought in great lumps on packhorse backs to the kiln. Here it was carried up a ramp and dumped into the top of the kiln, mixed in layers with culm (coal). Beneath this, in the eye of the kiln, a fire was kindled with brushwood and this caught the coal and burnt the lime into lumps of quicklime and lime ash. The kiln kept burning all summer if need be, and eventually burnt without culm from its own heat. The burnt lime was then loaded onto packhorses in canvas sacks or in lime pots, or piled into carts and carried to the field. Here it was put into great heaps covered with earth until it burst through. Then it was hacked into small pieces, loaded into a low cart (or 'butt') from which it was spread. All this was known as 'hacking of forrage'.

Quicklime was dangerous; there were some fearful accidents at kilns. At

Combe Martin, a man trod on the crust of the kiln and fell in up to his waist. He was eventually rescued, made drunk, and carried home to die, singing, so it was said, 'Nearer my God to thee' at the top of his voice. Likewise, it was believed that poor tramps sleeping beside a burning kiln on cold nights for the warmth, turned over in their sleep, fell in and were consumed completely.

Vancouver, writing in 1809, said that lime had only been used in the last sixty years. But he was quite wrong. Risdon and Westcote, in the early 1600s, refer to lime as newly introduced and 'answering better' and in 1630 John Stancombe of Ilsington is recorded as having 'lime pots and marlstones in a kiln', and a right of way to fetch lime. The monks of Tavistock never used lime, however, though they had both land that needed lime and land on limestone at Plympton and Denbury, where it could have been quarried and burnt. This would seem to date the first use of lime on the land to the sixteenth century.

Going to the kiln or to fetch sand was like a visit to the mill, an agreeable occasion. It probably involved waiting your turn and this gave a good chance for gossip and a drink. Lime burning was a thirsty business and kilns were often built with adjoining 'cellars' that often became a pub. Here there was a chance to listen to the news and sometimes perhaps to radical, even heretical, opinions. The cobbler was traditionally the local radical, but millers and lime burners met all sorts of folk, and could pick up unconventional ideas. Above all, the lime kiln was a warm and cosy venue for gossip. At Combe Martin men used to cook their breakfast eggs on the hot stones of the kiln as they waited and chatted.

Marl

Marl is a sort of clayey earth that, at its best, contains lime and adds body to light soils. It is not clay proper and it does not stick to the shovel. It was thought to be somehow 'hot' in the old sense of the medieval science of materials. It was used extensively only in east Devon. Colepresse called this part off Devon the 'marle country' and the Ordnance Survey map can reveal, and the eye can detect, numerous pits scattered all over the east Devon countryside. These are marl pits: far too numerous and big to be pits for digging earth for cob walling. Marlpits Lane in Honiton is only one of a number of indicative place names.

Marl was detected by noticing where springs broke out on a hillside where there was an impervious layer of rock or clay. It could also be found where stream banks 'roozed down' and by the 'curdlie cast' of the water in a stream. The deeper the marl the better the quality, but it was dear to get out. Once dug it was carried out into the fields by packhorse in marl pots that held 300 lb, and applied at the rate of 1200 to 1600 loads (c. 200 tons) per acre. Marling began at 'Rudemass', (3 May) and went on till Lammas, (1 August). It would take a packhorse team of seven 200 journeys to dress one acre, a very long job. The marl was then ploughed in, not too shallow or it would 'burn' the seed, or too deep for then it was lost. The best land to marl was flinty shallow land with lots of stones.

Vancouver refers to red and blue marl and says that farmers preferred the blue, though it 'fermented' much less with vinegar than the red. This indicated that Vancouver at least knew how to make a simple acid/alkali test, and suggests that the farmers knew it too, an indication of an early practical use of chemistry applied to agriculture. Marshall noted marl pits at Yarcombe big enough and old enough to be growing large oaks. He didn't think marl did much good and thought lime or just ground chalk to be better.

It is unlikely that marl was applied for two centuries or more without doing any good. There is plenty of available limestone in east Devon that could have been used instead of marl but seems not to have been. Marl appears to have been more than just a 'sweetener' of soil, since the marl at Hemyock, very extensively applied, has been shown to contain no calcium at all. The pastures on the top of the Blackdown Hills are rather better in quality than the soils would suggest; this may be due to marling and to the presence of 'marl grass', a strong species of white clover once often included in seeds mixtures. Marl seems to have had qualities that, though not measureable, are none the less real, and medieval farmers in east Devon somehow discovered this. The monks of Forde Abbey had marl pits, and there is a record of a death from suffocation in a 'marlera' near Uffculme as early as 1249.

Devon and Cornish farmers used all these dressings according to local availability. They had a reputation for dressing heavily and over the centuries they were able, in an unhelpful climate, to increase markedly the yields of corn on their often poorish land.

10.
Sowing the Seed

Hacking

Once the land was ploughed and dressed it was 'hacked'. Marshall thought this was 'one of the operations belonging to the established practice of the district which have so little resemblance to the practice of the island at large that they can scarcely be considered as belonging to British husbandry'. Hacking was no more than harrowing the ploughed soil by hand with a hacking mattock, not unlike a beat axe. A team of men worked their way along the ridges reducing the furrows to a good tilth and then shovelling up the soil of the furrows on top and removing any growing weeds. Marshall thought it amazing that this should be done by hand and attributed it to a time before ploughs came into common use when 'hand culture' was the rule. Such hand cultivation was known in Wales, Scotland, and Ireland and suggests that south-western farming had Celtic origins, or perhaps merely shared the same agrarian problems.

Hacking was laborious; ten acres of hacking took as long as fifty acres of conventional harrowing, but it was effective. It cleared the land and produced a good tilth. It was a communal activity needing five to nine men an acre; 'who had to have their drinkings and are little less pampered than in wheat harvest', noted Vancouver, who disapproved of all such festivities.

Sowing

Preparing land to grow wheat took a great deal of time and trouble. Ploughing or beat burning began in the early spring and the land was worked thoroughly throughout the summer. One useful practice was to harrow to a fine tilth and wait for a shower of rain; this would germinate all the weed seeds, and they could be killed completely by another stroke of the harrow, just when the 'whitey moors', the first fine white roots, showed. Sometimes turnips were sown at midsummer to be eaten off, the land well manured and trodden by the 'golden hoof' of the sheep flock. Then the wheat was sown in the winter after another ploughing. Winter wheat could be sown in quite cloddy soil, too fine tilth set hard in the winter rains, and the clods would break down in the frost. Spring corn could, and should, be sown in dust to give quick germination and growth. To get a good tilth required judgement. It was safe to plough the land wet before Christmas, but not after. After Christmas there was not enough time left for the frosts, rain and drying wind to break down the soil into a good tilth. Harrowing too wet a soil just produced sticky clods that dried iron hard and had to be rolled and harrowed many times. Land that had set hard had to be ripped up with a tormentor or spurtang. Soil caught just right fell apart into a fine tilth at the stroke of a harrow.

In Devon they liked to sow wheat late to avoid mildew, and give the crop a chance against charlock and other weeds 'in permanent residence', but in Cornwall wheat had to be as 'high as a hare' by Penhale Fair, 25 September. Spring barley ('cuckoo barley') could be sown as late as April when the cuckoo arrived. Carew wrote that 'in the westernmost parts of Cornwall they do carry their barley to the mill eight or nine weeks from the time that they sowed it, such an hasty ripening do the bordering seas afford.' Oats was almost invariably the 'farewell' crop, the last of the three corn crops before the land was laid down to grass. The grass and clover seeds were sown in the growing crop and needed a hard seedbed to germinate well. There were all sorts of varieties of corn, 'bearded Lammas' and 'ducksbill' wheat, grey, black and bearded oats, none of which survive today, but Fitzherbert knew of a variety of barley called 'sprott'. This must be the ancestor of a once famous, but now superceded, variety of barley called Spratt Archer. Way back in the fourteenth century the monks of Tavistock grew a variety of oats known distinctly as 'pillcorn'. It had a small yellow huskless grain; they continued to grow it even when new varieties were introduced, and it always fetched a good price. Remarkably, pillcorn under that very name, was still being grown in Cornwall in the last century. It may once have been the common cereal crop in the South West; perhaps it was from this that the disgusting beer was made.

Sowing was done by hand well into this century, either from a 'zillup' (seedlip) or from an apron, or by using a fiddle. Seed drills were known in Devon in the last century, but for a small farmer, a seed drill was too expensive to buy, and a contractor was unreliable. So the zillup remained long in use (plate 32). It was a flat-sided oblong basin, shaped to fit a man's body, with a strap to go over his shoulder. Seed corn in sacks was placed at carefully worked out intervals up and down the field, for refilling, so that the sower would not have to walk too far with his zillup empty. Often it was a two person job, with a woman or boy employed to keep the sower going without any delays. Seed corn was expensive, so the seed supplied had to cover the whole field evenly without any over at the end. It required some experience and judgement. A good man could sow a couple of pounds of clover seed, the finest seed, in an acre without any overlapping or surplus at the end.

The worst thing, the subject of infinite derision, was to leave unsown stripes across the field or some obvious double sowing. When land was ploughed in narrow ridges, it was probably fairly easy to ensure an even distribution; the sower merely adjusted his cast to the width of the ridge, which gave him easily visible guide-lines. But on a field with no ridges or very wide ridges, it was necessary to lay out markers. These were conspicuous peeled wands, set in the hedge or stuck in the ground, one at each end of the field, and often one in the middle, if the field was of any size. A marker had to be easily visible, as the sower had both to observe the width of his cast carefully and, at the same time, keep in the right line. He could cast with one hand or two. Two hands spread the seed more evenly, and the cast was done in time with the feet, left foot stepping forward and right hand casting, and vice versa. Using one hand, a man cast at every other pace, throwing the seed wide with the fingers, as well as the hand, quite open, with foot and hand agreeing. When a man got to the hedge, he marked the start of his next cast by pacing out the full width of his cast and making a footmark in the soil. He then placed his marker at that distance again, to come back to the next time. It was easy to make mistakes, only too visible when the corn came up.

The fiddle was used in the same way. It was a small sack on a framework, with a hole at the bottom, the size of which could be regulated. Beneath this was a round whirligig, divided into sections, that was rotated back and forth and cast out the seed by centrifugal force. It was powered by what looked like the bow of a violin, with a strong piece of cord fixed at either end of the bow and encircling a reel fixed below the whirligig. To sow, the labourer walked up and down the field, pushing the bow back and forth, fiddling! Some kinds of seeds would fly out further than others; the rate of sowing was adjustable; the speed of fiddling would alter the width of the cast and the amount of seed sown; so it was a job of considerable skill. With very small seeds, for example, clover or turnips, it was probably easier to sow evenly with a fiddle than by using the hands, but it was hard work walking a heavy load of seed across a rough cloddy tilth all day, often along or up steep hills. Seed corn was often dressed with lime in the past to guard against 'smut' a disease of wheat and this got in the eyes and nose. The worst thing was a strong gusty wind, which made accurate distribution very difficult. More accurate distribution was achieved eventually with the seed barrow, pushed by one man, with a land wheel that worked a worm to distribute the seed. But it could be used only on flattish ground. Sometimes seed was sown roughly, from the back of a cart, with a shovel. Eventually tractors did all the work, and the sower, that ancient archetypal figure of the annual miracle of seedtime and harvest, was seen no more in the land.

Harrowing was done with drag harrows with iron teeth. Oxen hated harrowing. 'It was great labour and pain to the oxen to go to harrow for it is better to go to plough two days than to harrow one day'. 'The ox is never woe, till he to harrow go', was an old saying. This was because, as Fitzherbert says, 'it went by twitches', the harrow jerked over the clods and was never a steady pull. If the land was very cloddy and could not be broken down with alternate harrowing and rolling, mallets were used to break the clods by hand.

Unless the seed was ploued in, it was never completely covered. This was an invitation to every rook, pigeon, or starling to take its free share. Traditionally, it was the job of the smallest children, armed with what became known later as a football rattle, and piles of stones, to scare off the birds. Children of four or five years old were left alone in the fields. Some adults were to remember with pain their lonely abandonment in a great field. Seed would germinate in ten days or so, but until then it was at risk. Scarecrows did some good, but birds in the end used them as perches. Eventually the more modern corn drill buried the seed almost completely out of reach and sight of the birds, and did the little 'tackers' and 'maids' out of a job. But there was work for them through the summer, clearing the corn of its innumerable weeds, the crimson and green corn cockle, the yellow corn marigold, the blue cornflower, the twining corn spurrey, the purple fumitory, the scarlet poppy, the pink restharrow, and the ever-present yellow charlock. Then it was time for harvest.

Rootcrops

Until a couple of hundred years ago, nearly all the farmer's crops were either cereal crops or legumes (that is peas and beans). Turnips were known by the seventeenth century, but were apparently little cultivated in the South West until the late eighteenth. However, a farm called Neopardy and a field called Nepland are recorded as early as 1249. These may contain the ancient Anglo Saxon word 'naep' meaning turnip. Around 1750, the enquiry sent to many parishes in Devon suggests that turnips were very little grown by then. Turnips were reported at Dolton, Meshaw, Roborough; and at Rose Ash the Rector replied that 'of late turnips have much improved our land. At Northam, where there 'were many acres for (market) garden uses, turnips were fit to be drawn at midsummer', probably to supply the needs of the port of Bideford. Egg Buckland did much the same to supply Plymouth. It is hard to believe that these were only places to grow turnips, particularly as Meshaw, Roborough, Rose Ash and Dolton are all parishes in central Devon, which was generally thought to be backward agriculturally. Some were being grown near Brixham, in fact on a field scale in 1688, since John Whittle who came over to Torbay with William of Orange's invading army in that year, wrote in his diary that he spent the night very uncomfortably in a turnip field. Having nothing else to eat, he and his comrades devoured some raw.

By Marshall's and Vancouver's day south-western farmers had taken to turnips pretty well. They are reported in every district, but they were badly grown. They were broadcast and not weeded with the hoe, or set out at intervals in any way. So they were liable to be very weedy, and this is one reason why they were sown so late. The normal time to sow was midsummer. One farmer said that before midsummer day was too soon after midsummer day was too late! They were grown often as a 'breaking' crop on the ashes of beat burning, which suited them very well, but they could be fitted in anywhere in the rotation. Those sown at midsummer were fed off by sheep or cattle, on the field most frequently, by November. The land, well fertilized by the dung and 'golden hoof' of the sheep, was then sown to wheat. It was even possible in favoured areas to sow turnips after harvest in the stubble of the corn. These were called brush turnips and they eked out the other turnip crop and filled 'the hungry gap' in the early months of the year. This was when the aftermath, (or the 'rouen') that is, the regrowth of fields cut for hay, had been eaten, and the new grass of the water meadows had not yet sprung into lush green growth.

Marshall thought the method of growing of turnips in the South West 'a disgrace to British agriculture'. He reported turnip fields yellow with charlock in autumn, and white with the silvery pods of the weed after it had shed its seed in December. Some folk tried to pull the weeds by hand, but he thought this took longer than hoeing, and that Devonshire husbandmen were supine, since turnips had been grown in the county for fifty years. There certainly seems to have been a reluctance to hoe, since Marshall, while he was running the Buckland Abbey estate, could not get his workmen to hoe the crop, unless he actually stood over them. However, he did see some well-hoed fields in the Exe valley and thought that hoeing was coming in slowly, and in the end got some women, who had never hoed before, to hoe properly at Buckland.

In the end south-western farmers learnt the value of hoeing, which produced a greater crop, and grew beautifully clean fields of turnips, mangels and swedes. The straight rows produced by the seed drill helped. Jethro Tull invented the first seed drill that planted and spaced seeds in a straight line. His was a single row drill, but in due course, drills were made that sowed two or three rows at once. These drills were pulled by a horse or tractor, and it was vital to get the rows as straight as possible by sowing to a mark, and coming back on the next bout accurately. Drills were wheeled and normally all that was needed was to keep the wheel exactly in the previous wheel mark.

There was one pest that had to be dealt with that caused immense trouble, the turnip fly. This devoured all the first leaves of the turnip, damaging the crop, sometimes almost totally destroying it. Often it had to be resown. There were supposed to be remedies, such as rolling the crop with a light roller or dragging paraffin soaked sacks or smelly elder branches over it. But Wiltshire people had it right when they sang,

> For the fly, the fly, the fly be on the turnip,
> And it's all my eye, for we to try, to keep fly off the turnip.

Hoeing

Hoeing was really two quite separate jobs. The first was to keep the spaces between the rows of turnips or other roots clean of weed. The second was to space out, to thin, the turnips so that each would grow to its maximum size, and to keep the spaces between each turnip also clean of weeds. Some folk put radish seed into the seed drill with the turnips or mangels. This germinates and shows up before the turnips in the row, and enables hoeing to take place sooner, before the real crop shows up, and just as weed seeds sprout.

Hoeing between the rows involved using a horse-drawn, or tractor-drawn hoe. This was designed with feet that cut through the roots of the weeds. The feet had to be sharp and polished to do a good job. There were two to each row, placed so that they would hoe on either side of the growing crop but leave it untouched. The horse pulling the hoe had to be led absolutely accurately, so that the hoe blades would not get out of line and cut off the crop instead of the weeds. The hoe itself was movable, within limits, on its frame; it had handles, which could be steered from side to side to shift the hoe blades to right or left. Both horseman and hoer had to concentrate hard if this was to be done satisfactorily. When done well it looked very good, the rows of swedes or turnips were left intact and growing, while the weeds between the rows were all quailed up and dying, and the newly stirred earth was clear. In a wet growing season, when the weeds were plentiful, this job had to be done twice or more. If the proper line was lost, the crop was ripped up and was the cause of much cursing and swearing.

With the rows done, the crop had to be hand hoed. Turnip and mangel seed germinates uncertainly, so it was not safe to assume that every seed would sprout. Hence it was necessary to oversow, to sow many more seeds than was necessary to produce a good crop. Generally more than were needed appeared, so a row of turnips would need half or more of its plants removing, and this had to be done by a hand hoe. So the summer months, often at hay harvest time, saw teams of men and women either gapping or singling turnips. Gapping meant hoeing out sufficient plants, thinning the row initially. Then to get a really good crop the plants had to be singled, so that each individual plant had sufficient room to grow. Gapping was easy, singling more tricky, but some men and women could use a hoe with great speed and dexterity, sliding the edge of the hoe between two tiny plants to remove one and leave the other undisturbed and intact and growing. This is like hoeing in a garden, but the difference lies in the fact that men and women had to do this for days on end, hoeing acre after acre of roots, with stiff and aching backs. Some people used to undertake this work on piece-rates, and contract to hoe a large field themselves, knowing that it paid to do the job fast. In fair conditions it took twenty-seven hours of work to hoe an acre, so the job required a lot of resolution. It tested a man's character, to be left alone day after day in a turnip field, singling turnips with an aching back. It was genuine hard work, although a weedless field of vigorous roots was something to take pride in. Labourers on piece-work would only take on a field if the crop was growing in a really good plum tilth, so that the hand hoer could shift the soil easily without any digging or hacking. Hoeing roots on hard soil was intolerable and it was up to the farmer to see that the field was in good condition. Well-hoed and strongly growing turnips also offered resistance to the dreaded turnip fly. Latterly a chemical seed dressing deterred the fly completely.

Roots filled the gap between the time the grass ceased growing in winter and the early bite of the water meadows. In much of England, it is probably true that surplus animals that could not survive the winter on the hay and straw and other feed available were slaughtered and their meat salted. This was known as Martinmas Beef, since it was killed about then, 11

November. It was a dainty at Easter tide, having been smoked up the chimney and salted, when there was not much else. How many cattle were killed at this time is not certain, but it may be that in the South West this was less necessary. Grass often goes on growing till Christmas and most south-western farms were principally grass. The coldest months are late January and February and it was at this time that the grass of the water meadows started to spring. So in the South West, the gap was fairly short and this may have been one reason why farmers were slow to grow turnips in Devon and Cornwall; they did not need them in the same way as other farmers.

11.
Corn Harvest

THE WHEAT BEING READY TO CUT down, and amounting from ten
to twenty acres, notice is given in the neighbourhood that a reaping is to
be performed on a particular day, when, as the farmer may be more or
less liked in the village, on the morning of the day appointed, a gang,
consisting of an indefinite number of men and women assemble at the
field and reaping commences after breakfast, which is seldom over till
between eight and nine o'clock. The company is open for additional
hands to drop in at any time before the twelfth hour, to partake of the
frolic of the day. By eleven or twelve o'clock the ale or cider has so much
warmed and elevated their spirits, that their noisy jokes and ribaldry are
heard to a considerable distance and often serve to draw auxiliary force
within the accustomed time. The dinner, consisting of the best meat and
vegetables, is carried into the field between twelve and one o'clock; this
is distributed with copious draughts of ale and cider; and by two o'clock
the pastime of cutting and binding the wheat is resumed and continued
without other interruptions than the squabbles of the party, until about
five o'clock, when what is called 'the drinkings' are taken into the
field, and under the shade of a hedgerow or large tree, the panniers
are examined and buns and cakes and all such articles are found, as the
confectionary skills of the farmer's wife could produce for gratifying the
appetites of her customary guests at this season.

After the drinkings are over, which generally consume from half to
three quarters of an hour (and even longer it if can be spared from
the completion of the field) the amusement of the wheat harvest is
continued with such exertions as draw the reaping and binding of the
field together with the close of the evening. This done, a small sheaf is
bound up and set upon the top of one of the ridges; when the reapers
retiring to a certain distance, each one throws his reap hook at the sheaf
until one, more fortunate or less inebriated than the rest, strikes it down;
this achievement is accompanied with the utmost stretch and power of

the voices of the company, uttering words very indistinctly but somewhat to this purpose. 'We ha in! We ha in!', which noise and tumult continue about half an hour, when the company retire to the farmhouse to sup, which being over, large portions of ale and cider enable them to carouse and vociferate until one or two o'clock in the morning.

At the same house, or that of a neighbouring farmer, next day, a similar scene is renewed and so continued through the precious season of the wheat harvest in this country. It must be observed that the labourers thus employed in reaping, receive no wages, but in lieu thereof, they have an invitation to the farmer's house to partake of a harvest frolic; and at Christmas, which seldom continues less than three or four days, the house is kept open night and day to the guests, whose behaviour during the time may be assimilated to the frolics of the bear garden.

This was 'harvest home' as Vancouver saw it in 1808. It had surely been something like this since there had been a harvest, on which local folk would have to rely for the rest of the year. It was to everyone's gain if the harvest was abundant and brought in safely. Corn would be cheap if all went well. Until the 1870s or so, it is likely that most people depended for their daily bread on locally grown wheat, so the harvest was everyone's concern, and it was natural that they should all join in. It was a great celebration, the culmination, the apex of the farming year, a feast to be relished and remembered from one year to the next; 'thic year us cut wheat for old maister Venner down Broad Park'. The celebration went on till Christmas; the farmer got all the labour he wanted free, in a spirit of good will, in return for plentiful food and drink.

Vancouver disapproved of it. It was 'attended with heavy expense'; 'it was disorderly'; 'it called for the strongest disapprobation and immediate discontinuance'! But it had a strong hold on country people. Many of the old village revels were stopped by the Victorian parsons in the nineteenth century. Baring-Gould's father stopped the revels at Lew Trenchard and started a church fête instead. The Church had to take note of the harvest, and did this by instituting Harvest Thanksgiving, about the only time in the year when the churches were full. However, for locals, surely that was not a patch on the 'harvest frolic', which continued alongside Thanksgiving for a good many years. A vestige of this communal festivity still survived, until the arrival of the combine harvester, in the threshing dinner, when the threshing machine came to the farm. Threshing required a lot of men (even with the machine), more than a small farm could muster, so neighbours came in and the farmer's wife supplied a huge meal of meat, potatoes and pudding in the farm kitchen for all the helpers. That was still going on in the 1950s, but the combine does the thrashing now; few men are needed, and the celebration of the harvest is quite gone.

Vancouver describes 'crying the neck'; the setting up of the last sheaf, well enough, but omits to notice that the final sheaf, the 'neck' was tied up elaborately and brought to the farm kitchen and hung from the beam or the clavel, till the next harvest. This is presumably the origin of the 'corn dolly', so popular in gift shops. Marshall knew the ceremony as the 'harvest holla'.

THE OLD FARM

Both terms are combined in this account written in 1832 by Mrs Bray, and published in her book, *The Borders of the Tamar and the Tavy*:

We were passing near a field where the reapers were assembled. In a moment the pony started, so sudden a shout came from the field. It was only the people making their games as they always did to the spirit of the harvest. When the reaping is finished towards evening the labourers select some of the last ears of corn from the sheaves. These they tie together and it is called the 'neck'. Sometimes this neck is decorated with flowers twisted in with the reed which gives it a gay and fantastic appearance. The reapers then proceed to a high place to 'holla the neck'. The man who bears this offering stands in the midst whilst all the other labourers form into a circle about him. Each holds aloft his hook and they all shout as loud as they can 'Ar nack, ar nack we have'n', we have'n'. This is repeated three times and the firkin is handed round between each shout. When the weather is fine different parties of reapers stationed on some height may be heard for miles around shouting as it were in answer to each other.

In Cornwall, in contrast, it seems that harvest dinners were held only by the rich, or as Carew called them, the 'good livers', and for their relations and neighbours, and lasted the best part of a week. In Suffolk, long after its significance was understood, the last sheaf was accompanied by demands for 'Largesse, largesse!' In Devon no such cries were needed, the largesse was evident and abundant.

What was not so popular was when millers bought the corn, so joyously harvested, and sold it out of the district in seasons of high prices. Both farmers and millers became intensely unpopular if that occurred. In some ways folk regarded locally grown corn as their own to eat during the ensuing winter, and selling it on at an obvious large profit 'broke the rules'. People had what they thought a legitimate way of dealing with this; they 'rioted', broke into the mill, took the corn they needed, and paid for it at what they thought was a 'just price'. There were such riots in the 1760s, and during the Napoleonic Wars, when corn prices reached starvation levels. Miners in Cornwall also took the law into their own hands in this way on occasions. At Harberton near Totnes the miller was threatened with a noose. These riots, however, may have been sparked off more by townsfolk who had no direct interest in the land and depended on wages only. Farm labourers often had access to some tail corn, or a bit of land and their own potatoes in bad times, and small farmers doubtless kept back enough to survive, but there was great bitterness in the country about the high prices of the war years.

Harvest began when the corn was ripe which was not easy to establish. Teeth and fingers and nose and tongue determined ripeness. Barley was most difficult; it seemed ripe when it hung down 'goosey necked', but that was not really right, as the goose needed to be dead to match the posture of the really ripe barley ear. 'If you think your barley is ripe, go away for three weeks, and then it might be', was perhaps better advice. Experience counted.

Wheat was cut with a sickle or a reap hook or 'yowing hook' (hewing hook), a large broad reap hook with a knob on the end of the handle. With one hand the reaper struck at the bottom of the wheat, with the other he pressed the wheat he was cutting against that still growing, then gathered together enough to make a sheaf in a sort of cone, and cut all that off at the bottom. Then the whole bundle was shifted with arm and hand to lie on the band, with which it was to be bound. This was some previously prepared 'reed' or just straw twisted together. The binding was often done by women, who followed the gang of reapers closely. It took four men to reap and one to bind an acre in a day.

Barley and oats were normally mowed with a scythe and not reaped. Barley straw was weak and thin and cut easily; with oats the nutritious straw had to be saved. Oats too, in the South West, were bound up with reed, unlike the practice in other counties where it were sometimes carted to the barn loose. This was because of the use of the pack saddle, which could not, unlike a waggon, prevent loose corn slipping through. If barley and oats were very 'rank' and had 'lodged' or 'gone lie' (that is been beaten down by the weather) then they too had to be reaped with a hook. It had once been the practice to cut off the ears of wheat very high and then mow the remaining straw for thatch or bedding. Whatever way it was done the fields had to be very carefully raked, often more than once, to avoid waste, and then the local folk, the 'harvesters', had the right to glean what was left.

Once the mechanical reaper and binder was introduced a corn field was cut all around the outside first. As the area of the uncut corn got smaller and smaller, there was always excitement, as here rabbits and hares and other game took shelter, only to flee at the last moment. Dogs and guns and boys were ready for them and it was even possible for a good runner to run a rabbit down in a big field. Colepresse described a more organized system.

> To prevent the mischief done by hares and rabbits affordeth them [the harvesters] some sport. For in grazing time, after the day is gone, they at their feeding they come, and set their nets, traps, hare pipes, and downfalls, at those places they purposely left open, having the day before secured all other places; when all is set with much silence, with one alotted to every trap, then with a great cry and noise of boys and dogs, they quickly rang the field, so that most part of the game is secured.

Rabbits were usually the property of those who killed them.

Before the corn could be carried, it had to dry. It did this in the stook or shock of about ten sheaves, put in a square, or in two rows with an upturned sheaf on top. In Cornwall they used to make small ricks of sheaves, 'arrish mows', in the field in the shape of a pyramid, with the base of the sheaves, often full of weeds and grass, outwards exposed to the wind and the 'dryth'. Corn in an arrish mow was thought to be safe from the weather. Ordinary stooks were much more exposed to the weather and had to be knocked down and remade regularly or the corn would sprout and grow green and spoil. 'Stooking' was an agreeable job, as the unstooked sheaves got fewer and fewer, but hard hands and covered forearms were necessary, as corn, in the old days, was often full of ripe blackened thistles, whose prickles hurt more, if anything, than those that were green.

Once dry, corn was carried, eventually in waggons or carts, to the barn or the rick. But before the nineteenth century in the South West, all corn was carried by packhorse, loaded on to two pairs of long crooks. Once, barley and oats, because they had been mown with a scythe, were tied into great trusses with four ropes, as much as two men could lift on to the pack-saddle. But by Marshall's day this was no longer done, all corn was bound into sheaves. Once loaded, a string of packhorses set off for the farmyard or mowstead. Here the corn was often housed directly in the threshing barn. In Colepresse's day they 'housed all' in Devon, but he said they made 'mowhays', groups of ricks, in Cornwall containing many hundred sheaves, where he considered that the corn dried better.

Ricks or mows in a mowstead or 'mustedge' became common enough in Devon later, and pitching the sheaves to the top of the rick required a special local skill. It was not possible to pitch from the top of a packhorse load, the horse would not stand still enough, or form a firm platform, so the corn was pushed off onto the ground or on to an old sail, and that meant a much higher pitch to the top of a rick. A special fork was designed with short sharply converging prongs, and men would pitch the sheaves over their heads to a great height. The carefully shaped prongs made the sheaf part from the fork, 'with a spring' and fly higher, or at least so it was believed. Young men competed at this and 'achieved an extraordinary degree of flight and expertness'.

Devonshire ricks were often square but the roof was sloped, hipped, all round, not just front and back as was common elsewhere. They, like hay stacks, took skill to make, and they were thatched immediately with 'reed' and ropes of straw. These were tied in to the roof of the rick with doubled back hazel spars, inserted pointing upwards, and pushed right home, to shed rain.

Threshing

Once safely housed or ricked, the next work to be done was threshing. By Vancouver's day thrashing machines were becoming fairly usual in Devon. Vancouver thought that anyone with fifty to sixty acres of corn found them advantageous. These were barn threshers, normally powered by horses or a water mill and they would thrash out six bushels, or more than three hundredweight of wheat, and nine of barley or oats per hour, with six men in attendance. Fifty or sixty acres of corn implies a farm size of three to four hundred acres at least, and this was rare in the South West. So these machines were useful to big farmers, who may, of course, have had hired them out to smaller men on occasion.

For anyone with a few acres only, machine threshing was made possible by the introduction of the towed wheeled thresher. This was still in almost universal use at the end of the last war. Contractors hauled these around from farm to farm during the winter, often using the old single cylinder Field Marshall Diesel Tractor, that could be heard thumping away miles off.

This both towed and provided power. Before that, the thresher was pulled by a steam traction engine, and there are hair-raising stories of threshing rigs, steam engine, thresher and trussing machine getting out of control and careering down a steep hill.

A thresher required ten men, one to feed the corn, one to cut the binds, two on the sacks of threshed grain, one to clear the douse (the rubbish) under the drum, two at least to carry away the trussed straw and three to fork sheaves to the feeder off the rick. The contractor tended to his tractor or steam engine and did little else, and the 'maister' supervised. For all the maister's wife had to supply a threshing dinner of vast proportions. Feeding the drum could be dangerous; hands, arms and even legs were lost down the feeding hole, where the heavy toothed drum rotated at great speed. It was a noisy, dusty, dirty but festive occasion, something to be looked forward to, unless the corn had been ricked damp and gone mouldy. Then there were clouds of black stifling dust – the best possible source of 'farmer's lung' – and a source of shame to the farmer.

Ricks were built on layers of faggots to keep them dry, or on staddle-stones or wooden frameworks to keep rats and mice out. But nothing really stopped those vermin and the last stages of threshing was always accompanied by the shrieks and yells of yelping dogs and cursing men, as the rats fled as best they could, in a hazardous whirl of prongs and sticks.

That kind of threshing lasted for not much more than a century and a half, from about 1800 to 1950. Before that there had been millenia of beating out the corn by hand with a flail (or 'drashel') or against a barrel, as it is still done today over much of the Third World. The Devonshire drashel was made of two pieces of wood joined together by a sort of universal joint of wood or leather (fig. 32). The beating piece was made of dense holly that would not split, the handle of strong ash. The corn was thrown down onto the threshing floor and beaten with the flail till all the grain was separated from the straw. Often there were four threshers at work keeping time 'performing a peal'. It was said that it was easy to tell how the work was being paid for by the speed of the blows, day work slow, piece work fast. Working too fast might result, for the unskilled, in a sharp tap on the skull from the business end. Many men spent day after winter day in the threshing barn, beating out, little by little, wheat for flour, or to sell when rent day was due; barley to make barley bread, or beer, or sell to a brewer if the sample was good enough to malt; oats for 'girts', or for the animals. Black smutty wheat 'flew abroad', burst, at the touch of the flail and spread like lamp black 'which is as visible in black smutty faces of the sweaty reapers as 'tis pleasant to behold'. The by-product of threshing, the loose douse, beaten out of the ears, filled the douse beds on which many slept. Until threshing was done a farmer did not really know how his corn had yielded, how good a harvest he had had, what his profits might be. Before this century a good yield would be 13–15 cwt; today it might be four times that.

Threshing was dry indoor work for the short days of winter, and was a sure source of employment at an otherwise dead time of the year. This is why the threshing machine was so unpopular; all the work could be done at once in a few days, and then there was no other work. The new threshing machine was one major cause of the Captain Swing Riots, the Last Labourers Revolt, in 1829, when many threshing machines were burnt by angry labourers, done out of regular winter work. There were a few burnings of machines and threatening letters in Devon, but not on the scale of Wiltshire or Hampshire, Dorset, Kent and Sussex.

In the South West, where thatch was still the usual rural roofing material until the late nineteenth century, there was a method of threshing to produce straw or reed for thatching. This was done by hanging up bundles of wheat or rye, tied just below the ears, by a rope from the barn roof. Only the ears had been beaten; the straw was carefully left untouched. This was then combed and rid of its weeds and grass, and straightened, using a long toothed rake. The resulting reed was punched upon the floor, till the butt of all the straws were level. These were then tied into tidy 'niches' of reed of 36 lb each. Fitzherbert knew of this practice of producing reed in Somerset, around 'Zelchester and Martok'. Oats and barley were thrashed without this nicety, their straw being useless for thatching. Later on, machines did the job of reed-combing.

The last work with corn was to winnow it, to separate the grain from the chaff. Marshall reports that in the South West,

> farmers of every class carry their corn into the field on horseback, perhaps a quarter of a mile, to the summit of some airy swell, where it is winnowed, *by women*; the mistress of the farm being exposed in the severest weather to the cutting winds of winter in this slavish and truly barbarous employment. The obsolete practice of the northern extremity of the island, in which farmers loaded their wives and daughters with dung to be carried to the fields on their backs, was but a little more uncivilised.

Devonshire farmers clearly had a more prosaic view of women's role on the farm than Marshall; the wind was free, and as Fitzherbert said, 'a wife should not be idle at no time'. All that was involved in winnowing was to throw the corn and chaff into the air from a basket, catch the corn again, and let the wind blow the lighter chaff away. (Barley, however, had long hard awns or ails that would not detach or blow away, and these had to be cut off with a 'barley aler'). But it cannot have been pleasant to stand, 'cold as a winnow', on the top of a winnowing down, tossing corn all day in the winter wind. In fact fans and winnowing machines were well in use by Vancouver's day, and Thomas Blampin even had 'a mill to clense corn' on his farm at Gittisham, as early as 1622.

12.
Haymaking

BEFORE THE INTRODUCTION OF ROOT crops, cattle lived on hay and straw in winter; even sheep would eat hay if hungry, though they tended to find a dollop of hay good only to lie on. By September a farmer needed to be able to look at his barn and his ricks and estimate if there was enough there for the winter to come, and more. Anyone farming for some seasons would have a year's supply of hay in hand from previous years, to cope with bad haymaking seasons, or droughts, or exceptional winters. There had to be enough to feed the plough oxen. If they could not plough there would be no bread corn and on that everyone depended. In real arable country, 'champion' open field country, hay was made almost entirely on the wet meadows.

Meadow land was the most valuable type of land. Even in the grassy South West, where hay could be cut in the ley grass fields, this was so, At Stokenham in 1309, meadow was worth 2s. per acre, while arable was worth 4d. an acre and pasture 3d. an acre. Stokenham was no exception. Meadow land was the most valuable because of the necessity to make hay and because, by its very nature, such land was scarce. Because of this high value, the practice arose of creating deliberately watered, irrigated meadow, using land as meadow that would normally have been rough pasture. These hillside watered meadows, normally used for ewes and lambs to graze in early spring, could also be cut for hay. Meadow hay made in natural meadows was known as 'land' hay, and the meadow had to be shut off from stock by March at the latest. Sheep or cattle breaking into a meadow caused much trouble, the growing hay was trodden down and made much more difficult to cut, and was eaten and spoiled.

In the South West hay was also made in what were called the 'upland meadows'. These were the ley fields, sown to grass and clover after corn, often grazed in the first year to make a good sward, and then cut regularly, for hay. This hay was known, in its first years of cutting, as 'seeds' hay. Meadow hay was finer and sweeter; it contained more herbs and many natural, not sown, grasses, such as sweet vernal grass, meadow foxtail, and meadow fescue, and was perhaps more palatable to stock. Making meadow hay or land hay in good condition, produced that ineffable delicate hot sweet scent, so characteristic of the old farming, but agony to hay fever sufferers. Seeds hay was mainly rye grass, and red and white clover. Cattle relished the different herbs in meadow hay, and will always pick out such 'weeds' on the hedgebanks to eat, rather than the sown grasses, if given a chance. Fitzherbert even says that the best hay and the sweetest for horses and beasts, was known as 'quich' hay, made out of 'crowfoot', a kind of buttercup that would grow a half a yard high. But such hay took a lot of making, it had to be dead dry, 'or else he will be-piss himself and wax hot and dusty'.

Haymaking really began in the early spring; the land had been dressed and manured in winter, and now the field was shut off from stock. At the same time, all sticks and stones had to be picked up that would otherwise blunt a scythe, and the mole hills, the 'want' hills, or as some said, the 'unty tumps', had to be levelled. This levelling was not, however, good practice in the water meadows that were to be grazed, particularly if they lay wet.

> Then bear with the mole hill, though thick it be set,
> That lamb may sit on it and so to sit dry,
> Of else to lie by it, the warmer to lie.

Cutting hay began in June and July and went on until all the hay was made. Haymaking clashed with working the ground in summer for next season's corn, and with sowing and hoeing turnips, weeding corn and sheep shearing. But only part of the day could ever be used for making hay. In the morning, in fine weather, the dew lay on it and the dew began to settle again in the evening too, so hay making was limited to the middle hours of the day. Hay was cut with a scythe, tight to the ground. It is impossible to describe how to use a scythe well, the art has to be learnt by practice. It was vital to have a scythe really sharp, it made all the difference, and so in a hay field, or in a barley field, where a scythe was also often used, it was usual for men to stop work regularly to sharpen their scythes, with a whetstone or a strickle. This last was, roughly, a wooden blade to which rough coarse sand paper had been stuck. The former was a carefully shaped piece of sandstone, cut and shaped to fit the hand. Devon produced some of the best whetstones in the country, known as Devonshire 'bats', dug from tunnels in the hillside near Blackborough in east Devon, and sold all over England in the nineteenth century. With one of these, a man sharpened his scythe till it felt smooth and silky to his thumb, working the whetstone on either side of the blade with swift strokes, till the blade got warm. The sound of sharpening would ring across the field. It was another art to be learnt.

Mowing was done as a team, with eatings and drinkings (probably plenty of cider) as refreshment; it was dusty work. As much hay was cut as could be made easily with the folk available. The hay was cut and laid in swathes, and then followed the actual making. Fitzherbert's advice given

450 years ago, is still good, allowing for the fact that now all is done by machine.

Also in the later end of June is time to begin to mow, if thy meadow be well grown; but howsoever they be grown, in July they must needs mow, for divers causes. One is that it is not convenient to have hay and corn both in occupation at one time. Another is, the younger and the greener that the grass is, the softer and the sweeter it will be when it is hay, but it will have [need] the more withering; and the older the grass is the harder and drier it is, and the worse for all manner of cattle; for the seeds be fallen and it is the harder to eat and chew. And another cause is, if dry weather come, it will dry and burn upon the ground and waste away.

When thy meadow be mowed, they would be well tedded [tossed and turned] and laid even upon the ground, and if the grass be very thick, it would be shaken with hands or with a short pitchfork. For good tedding is the chief point to make good hay, and then shall it be withered all alike; and when it is well withered on the over side and dry, then turn it clean before noon, as soon as the dew is gone. And if thou dare trust the weather, let it lie so all night; and on the next day, turn it again before noon, and towards night make it into windrows and then in small haycocks and so to stand one night at the least, and sweat. And on the next fair day cast it abroad again, and turn it once or twice, and then make it in greater haycocks, so to stand one night or more, so that it may sweat. For if it sweat not in the haycocks, it will sweat in the mow [rick] and then it will be dusty and not wholesome for horse, beasts or sheep. And when it standeth in the haycocks, it will be better to load.

Today hay is made in the same way. It must be dry before it is baled or put in a rick. If it is damp because it still contains sap, then it will heat in the bale or rick. It will either go brown – 'mow-burnt' – and then cease heating as it becomes dry, or if there is a lot of sap in it still, it can catch fire and the whole rick is lost. If the hay has been properly made and has no sap in it, but is damp because it has been rained on, then it is 'water wet', and when ricked like this, it will grow 'a filthy stinking mould' and become dusty as Fitzherbert describes. It was possible to deal with a heating rick, by boring large holes in it with a huge auger screwed down into the rick by hand. This allowed the heat to escape. Some heating was acceptable; brown mow-burnt hay was quite sweet, and coarse herbage, ('mere sedges',) could be made into quite palatable hay by a bit of mow-burn. It took, again, a lot of judgement to know just when to begin carting the hay. Too green and damp, too 'doney', and there was the risk of the rick catching fire. Hay could also be dried out too much in hot sunny weather and lose its goodness.

Certainly, instant decisions had to be made if the weather threatened rain. 'You ought, if possible, to be too quick for the weather, and your best time of carriage is but part of the day, for mornings and evenings are unfit.' You had to have men and horses and implements ready at all times to take advantage of any good weather. Grass, once turned and tedded and then rained on, went black pretty soon and was useless. If it was left unturned in the swath, and was then rained on, it would be a long time before it went off, but of course the growing grass grew through it in wet weather and made tedding and turning difficult. It was an anxious time for farmers. If the crop was lost, then, probably, so was much other hay being made in the parish, and hay would be dear. Old hands at the game used to say 'Don't worry, be patient, a time will come', and it generally did. Even in wet Devon it was possible not to spoil any hay year after year.

Thomas Tusser regarded haymaking as something of a military operation.

Go muster they servants, be Captain thyself,
Providing them weapons and other like pelf,
Get bottles and wallets, keep the field in the heat
The fear is as much as the danger is great.

With tossing and raking and setting on cocks.
Grass lately in swathes is fit for an ox,
That done, go and cart it and have it away,
The battle is fought, ye have gotten the day.

Machinery made it easier. By the end of the nineteenth century there were all sorts of hay turners, tedders, rakes, sweeps and grabs invented to machanize the making of hay. A tedder just threw the hay into the air and it fell in the same row. A hay turner turned over a whole swath at a time, exposed the undersurface to the sun, and moved the swath to one side on to dry ground at the same time. Rakes raked it into windrows ready to be cocked or carted. In difficult weather, the hay could be turned two or three times a day with a turner, and the whole process speeded up. In recent times no cocking went on, but the hay was ricked or baled direct from the turned swathe. But the basic principles of hay making remains exactly the same as it was in Fitzherbert's day.

South-western haymaking was done conventionally enough. Marshall had nothing much to observe about the process; it was the same as elsewhere, but he thought the scythe used was too short and 'laid in too near the handle'. The 'prong' or 'prang', the hay fork or pitchfork, he thought was 'ridiculously too small, fitted more for the hands of a cook than a haymaker; the tines are not longer than those of a Man of War's beef fork'. But as usual he had to admit that they had some merits, since they were designed for horse and crook husbandry, which was still prevalent in his day. Like everything else on the farm in the South West, hay was fetched in on the back of packhorses. Hay and corn were loaded between two pairs of long crooks rather like a stack and, indeed, one observer said that a well loaded packhorse disappeared beneath the load, so that when it moved, it looked as if a whole stack of hay was moving of its own accord! Marshall thought this was terribly old fashioned and attributed their continued use to the fact that no one had bothered to make any decent roads, suited to wheeled carriages. There were, he said, level farms without a pair of wheels where carts could have been easily used. He admitted that packhorses did a good job on hilly land, where carts drawn by horses might easily tip if heavily loaded, and said that in some cases they did as quick a job as

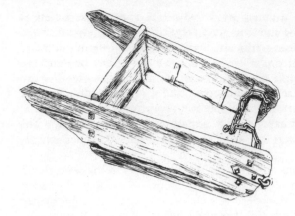

Fig. 29. Sledge for carriage on steep terrain

Fig. 30. Three-wheeled butt cart. The third wheel was made for stability.

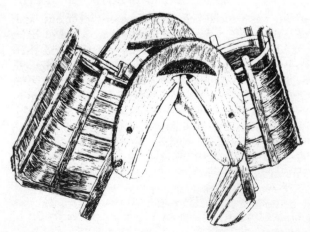

Fig. 31. Pack saddle with dung pots. These had hinged openings at the bottom and were a universal means of carriage for loose materials.

a cart. He compared the work of a lad and two packhorses with that of two men with three horses and a waggon, both carrying faggots the same distance. The two packhorses transferred twelve dozen faggots in a day and the waggon transferred forty-eight dozen. But the cost of the boy and the packhorses was 1s. 6d., while that of the waggon and three horses and two men was five shillings. Each dozen faggots cost a penny ha'penny, done by packhorse, while each dozen shifted by waggon, cost one penny and a fifth, 'the disparity of expense will not be found considerable'. The packhorses, in this case were not fully loaded and had a steeper journey than the waggon.

In fact, there were wagons on farms in Devon well back in the seventeenth century. At least eighteen of the Devon inventories list 'a pair of wheels' among other implements. Most of these were the property of rich gentlemen or yeomen, but not all. Katherine Lane of Crediton had a pair of 'waine' wheels amongst her possessions, the total of which was worth £125 in 1646, and William Wotton of Bickington had 'one iron bound wayne with a toomb tree' in 1601, and he was worth £177. The poorest man to possess a cart or waggon of some sort was Humphrey Jeffrey of Cookbury, yeoman, who died worth only £50, but left two pairs of iron bound wheels in 1647. It is possible that some of these wheels, with no wain or waggon mentioned, were the wheels of a timber carriage for fetching large tree trunks out of woods.

No hay ricks are made now, except ricks of bales. To the layman, who has seen a rick, it would not be obvious that some skill was required in the making. When making the rick, the sides had to have an outward batter in order to shed water, and this meant that each layer of hay had to be placed slightly overhanging. This would slide off, unless it was tied in with another layer placed on it, slightly back from the edge, and both these layers had to be both well trodden down and kept up. The centre had to be filled too, so that it would tie in the rest. In a badly made rick, the corners fell out and the whole thing had to be built again, to everyone's fury. So it took experience and application to make a rick, and even cart loads of hay had to be made in this way.

Haymaking, like harvest, was a social occasion; the word went out, as it still does to some extent, that a field was to be carried or cocked or bales were to be fetched in and the neighbours turned up: farmers and their wives and daughters and sons; everyone from the parish who could wield a prang; other farmers' men, too, if they were free in the evenings after work. It was a gathering, and the farmer's wife would be on her mettle, feeding the throng in the field. It was to everyone's interest, one way or another, to get the hay saved; and there was perhaps a load of firewood as a reward in the winter, or some dung for the garden, or a bidding to the harvest supper. There was surely cider, and tea, and cakes, and pasties, and a great lot of gossip and teasing, and many invitations to the young maidens from the men, to come and 'sweeten the hay', on the concealing, sweet-scented, yielding bed of the top of a hayrick.

13.
Livestock

FARM LIVESTOCK MUST OWE THEIR origins ultimately to local wild breeds. Domesday Book records the existence of wild ponies on some of the moors of the South West and these must be the forbears of the Exmoor and Dartmoor ponies. There may still have been wild sheep and pigs and cattle in the woods and on the moors at that date also, from which the present day breeds derive.

Unless they farmed on a very small scale farmers generally kept a mixture of livestock: cattle, sheep, pigs and a horse or two. Quite apart from their obvious products and uses it was believed that only such a mixture of these animals kept the farm healthy and the land in order. 'Beasts alone, nor horses alone, nor sheep alone, will not eat a pasture even', and sheep alone or cattle alone in any quantity also increased the risks of loss from disease. Besides these factors, the vagaries of the market could be got over to some extent by having a variety of animals to sell.

Cattle

The two existing breeds of Devon cattle are red, the Red Ruby of north Devon and the more orange South Devons or South Hams. These were recognized types by the beginning of the last century and the South Devon in particular became the standard Cornish cattle eventually. These were relatively recent developments. There is some evidence to suggest that local cattle were once often small and black rather like Kerrys or perhaps Dexters or the Welsh Black, Celtic cattle in fact. In the middle of the eighteenth century black cattle were being driven down from Dartmoor to St Budeaux to fatten for the Plymouth market and in 1811 Worgan described the native Cornish breed as being 'very small, black, short-nosed, coarse-boned. I saw black cows and bulls weighing only three to four hundredweight'. The Rector of Chivelstone in the South Hams, replying to Dean Milles' enquiries, wrote that 'our cattle are of a pretty large size, except those that are kept on the commons which are smaller', perhaps like the ones that Worgan saw. Some of these may have been not too remote from wild cattle. Carew wrote that 'some gentlemen suffer their beasts to run wild in their woods and waste grounds, where they are hunted and killed with crossbows and pieces in the manner of deer and by their fierceness and wariness seem to have put on a part of the others' nature'. These sound like very undomesticated cattle indeed. Marshall thought that Devonshire cattle, their colour apart, 'perfectly resemble the wild cattle which are still preserved at Chillingham Park in Northumberland'. These still survive as Park cattle and their colour is generally white.

In fact, the replies to Dean Milles' enquiries seem to indicate that the general run of Devonshire cattle around 1750 was black. To his question about the nature and colour of the local cattle there were forty-three replies indicating colour. These replies were well distributed, and all but nine of them describe the cattle as black. The nine exceptions reported cattle of a red or brown or fallow colour and all but one were from the South Hams or Torbay. Even around Molland, the cattle were reported as black, and that parish was the home of the Quartly family of Great Champson, the reputed founders of the red North Devon breed. They were also reported as black at Torrington and North Molton and generally over north Devon. This is puzzling; there are no known importations of red cattle, such as the forbears of the Sussex, Red Poll, Hereford or Norfolk breeds into Devon, though there were some Lincoln Reds at Powderham c. 1750. It is just possible that the respondents to Dean Milles were using the fairly commonly used term 'black cattle' in a general way, referring to nondescript unbred, unselected cattle in contrast to carefully selected pedigree stock. What makes this unlikely is that the question asked specifically refers to colour, and in the reply the high quality of the cattle is almost invariably praised.

Black cattle, then, were dominant in 1750, although by that date there was clearly a nucleus of red-brown cattle in the South Hams, no doubt the first South Devon, or South Hams or the 'old Marlborough Reds'. By 1796 Marshall wrote enthusiastically of Devon cattle, 'in many respects the most perfect breed of cattle in the island and the best workers I have anywhere seen'. Marshall did not make much distinction between the two Devon breeds, but to Vancouver the difference was clear and the North Devon was a red beast, redder and much meatier than the South Devon and producing much less milk. Tests have shown that the two breeds are related and there may well be an addition of Channel Island blood (Jersey or Guernsey) into the South Devon which might account for the high butter fat and yellow colour of the milk, similar to that of those two breeds. In north Devon the Quartly family were selecting and breeding the original Red Rubies at least by the beginning of the nineteenth century, and there were other breeders like the Davys of Rose Ash and many of the greater landowners. There were, at about the same date, local varieties of the Devon, some with the white spine of the Hereford and white on the udder, some, like the Widecombe Devon, adapted to moorland conditions, and some crossed with other breeds for the dairy as in east Devon. There were Devons in the Vale of Taunton and even a Cornish Devon! Breeding was the business and hobby of the richer farmer or the landowner; the ordinary farmer or dairyman bought what was available at market. Under the old three-life lease it was frequent for the landlord, right up until the nineteenth century, to demand and get the 'heriot' at the death of a tenant. This was the best beast in the man's herd, handed over without payment to the landlord, a relic of the times when a lord armed his men with war gear (heregeat) which he reclaimed on a man's death. This custom was said in 1750, to be a 'great hindrance to good breeding'.

Along with these 'red' cattle it is clear that there were in Devon and Cornwall, at least until the early nineteenth century, small black cattle that were perhaps well-suited to the moorland commons, the kind that Worgan saw. These have quite disappeared in the last century and a half and are extinct. The surviving printed inventories list cattle in plenty, but seldom refer to colour and never to breed. However Joseph Clarke of Marlborough in the South Hams had a red cow and a calf and a red steer in 1684 along with a black cow too, while James Holmead of Cruwys Morchard had black oxen, a black cow and black steers in 1678, among other cattle, and the black cattle were of greater value than the rest of his beasts.

Most farmers kept a cow or two to milk and further animals to breed. Their offspring would be used for ploughing and to fatten and sell if they lived on good ground. On poorer land there would be little fattening and the animal crop would be of store beasts, to be sold to others to fatten. There was a great market in Somerset for store beasts that would fatten on the Somerset marshes and be sold on to Bristol, and even London. Plymouth was another great market for beef and pork to be salted for the Navy, though Plymouth salt beef had a bad reputation below decks. When the railways came, the up-country markets opened out for south-western farmers and small cattle markets sprang up near railways. A great deal of Devon beef went north and east. Devon cattle were immensely admired and won all sorts of prizes at national shows, but their owners were criticized for fattening their best heifers for sale, and keeping the less good for breeding.

Dairying was a profitable activity in some parts of the South West. East Devon was a dairy area; butter factors in Honiton sent butter in tubs to Bath and London. A farmer did not, in this sort of market situation, milk his own cows; he let a dairy to a dairyman. The dairyman paid the farmers so much a cow; for this return the dairyman got the use of a house for himself, a dairy and a shippon, the cows, two and a half acres of land per cow for grazing and hay, and the calves as well. The milk was made into butter and sold, and the farmers supplied fuel for heating the coppers and raising the cream. Some big farmers had a number of farms and let them all out in this way. Profit depended on the price of butter. Dairies in east Devon comprised up to forty cows. In Cornwall the same practice prevailed, though on a much smaller scale. A man could rent five cows or fewer, sell the cream or butter, and got in return grazing land, some turnips, straw, turves, faggots and a small piece of potato ground and, if he rented more than five cows, a house as well. The skim milk fed the pigs kept by the dairyman. There were settlements of these small dairymen round many big farms in west Cornwall. This system was early specialization and not the rule. Most farmers looked on cattle as suppliers of milk, cheese and butter for themselves and to sell at the local market. When cash was needed there was a ready sale for any fattish beast, calves and old oxen included. Cattle, if kept and fed indoors, were the principal suppliers of dung, and there was the occasional animal to kill and salt for the house.

Cattle dropped their calves naturally in spring, and most were good mothers and tended their calves well. Calving, however, was not just left to nature. It was always best to have the calving house near the farmhouse, and of course on Dartmoor and elsewhere, where there were longhouses with cattle at one end, the cows were as close as may be to the farmers. It was once believed that a cow would milk much better if she could see and feel the house fire, and this may help to explain the survival of the longhouses in cattle rearing areas like Dartmoor. In Devon and Cornwall the word for the cowhouse is the 'shippon'. So it is in Lancashire and thereabouts, but in between, there is a large area where the word is simply cowhouse, and further north it is of course the 'byre'. Students of linguistics suggest that shippon was once the universal old word, and that it became superseded by cowhouse and similar words many centuries ago, except in remote Devon and Lancashire. It is a curious useage as it must originally have meant a sheep pen.

South Devons were prone to have difficult births, and farmers often had to spend nights (it was always nights) with their arms deep inside a cow trying to get the calf's head in the right place for birth, or coping with other such problems. Occasionally calves had to be heaved out by main force with ropes attached to the fore feet. There were no real vets until recently, though there was generally someone in the parish who knew a bit more or had a skill and could be summoned. Diseases were pretty well incurable and were numerous: 'quarter evil', 'red water', 'cattle plague', foot and mouth, 'inflammation'. Cows bloated on too much clover, were spiked in the stomach to release the pressure that would otherwise kill. One remedy for the 'scours' (diarrhoea) in calves, was to put a piece of very hard quartz in the calf's milk once it was on the bucket. This hard stone, so it was believed, would communicate its 'hardness' to the animals digestive system. This was pure sympathetic magic! Calves were reared on milk, then skim milk, and, by some farmers, on 'hay tea', that is hay in hot water. A farm of sixty acres might have eight to ten cows and a yoke of oxen, as well as rear all the young stock: some twenty to thirty cattle in all.

Sheep

The origins of south-western sheep are even more uncertain than those of cattle. There are, or at least were, some thirty to forty sheep breeds in this country. Each was particularly suited to the climate and vegetation of its own area and had presumably been selected and developed over the centuries for this purpose. Six local breeds are still recognizable in the South West. The Devon Longwool, the South Devon and the Dartmoor Grey Face are all long wooled sheep without horns, fairly indistinguishable from each other to the lay eye. Their country is west and north-west Devon, the South Hams, and the southern borderlands of Dartmoor respectively. There are two horned breeds, the Dartmoor Whiteface, and the Exmoor Horn. These are moor sheep, but on Dartmoor the Scotch Blackface has largely taken the place of the Dartmoor Whiteface. Finally there is the Devon Closewool, which is a recent, deliberately fixed cross between the Longwool and the Exmoor Horn. For many years farmers have crossed these native breeds with ones from other parts of Britain such as the Old and New Leicester and the Cotswold. More recently, many new breeds have been created by crossing foreign sheep such as Romanov, Friesland, Spanish Merino and others with the native breeds. It is now rare to see pure-bred flocks of the older breeds.

By modern standards the sheep of the past were a skinny lot of runts. The Tavistock monks could shear no more than 2lb of wool per sheep from their flocks. South Devon sheep now commonly cut about 15lb or more, and a ram's fleece might weigh 30lb. In Cornwall, Worgan took a good look at the native Cornish sheep, which were probably as near the native local breed as may be. They had grey faces, coarse short thick necks, stood lower before than behind, had narrow backs, flat sides, with fleeces weighing 2–3 lb, no more than the Tavistock monks got 300 years before his day. Worgan also refers to 'mongrel' flocks on the 'downs' of about the same size, some with horns, which would eat anything but were much afflicted with 'scab'. What might be called Towan sheep, that lived on the sand dunes, or 'towans', at Perranporth and Gwithian, eating the coarse grass, relished chomping up the innumerable snails that lived on the grass. These sheep were small, too, with fleeces of 2–3 lb. Carew thought that Cornish sheep had been improved in his day, from the time when the wool they bore was not wool at all but 'Cornish hair'. They were, now, he thought, 'big of mould, fine of wool, breeding often, fattening speedily and selling well'. Those, doubtless, were sheep from the enclosed lands near Plymouth, where he lived. Local, unimproved, sheep from the moors were much as they always had been, long after his day. By 1809 it was possible to distinguish four local breeds in Devon: the Exmoor and Dartmoor (both horned), the Bampton Nott and South Devon Nott, so called because they did *not* have horns. The fleeces of these breeds weighed 7–8lb, or 10lb in the case of the South Devons.

Farmers with water meadows or with land where the grass came up early aimed at early fat lambs. A meadow, closed off from stock and well watered from October, could carry up to twenty ewes and their lambs per acre from the beginning of February until early April when the grass started to grow well elsewhere. Sheep had to have a dry field adjoining, to lie out on. After April the meadow could be watered again and laid up for hay. After cutting it would carry stock until September or October again. This was why water meadow was so valuable; early fat lambs, Easter lambs, fetched a very good price and they could really only be produced using the meadows. Fat lamb was almost the only sure profit in bad times. Clearly the watering, cutting and maintenance of gutters took a lot of time and skilled knowledge. This practice has quite disappeared, though the gutters survive to be seen in many places.

Farmers with less good land had to be content with lower prices or rear store sheep for fattening on elsewhere. For those who had access to moorland, it was possible to pasture sheep, cattle ('rother beasts') and horses ('widge beasts') on the moors for a payment. Great numbers of sheep and cattle were 'agisted', pastured, in this way on the moors, to free the inland fields for hay or other stock, and to get the animals out of the bite of flies. There were moormen who used to 'cry the moor', announce in all the villages when the moor was open, and the lanes would then be full of bleating flocks making their way to the windy healthy moor. All sheep had to be marked with a cut in the ear, an 'ear mark', or with raddle, and it was the moorman's job to make a 'drift', to drive and 'tell', count, the sheep every so often, to see that all were marked. Ewes and lambs were brought down to the lower country in November or so but the wether flocks were often left until really cold weather set in. No one now eats wether mutton; all the male lambs are fatted off as lamb, but in the past the moor abounded with wether flocks that stood the cold and picked up what they could for three or four winters. Mutton from them was the very best. Farmers who used the moors in this way regarded their bit of moor as their own and 'dogged off' strangers' sheep.

A good shepherd really did known his sheep. A man could say of a ewe, 'she had two lambs last year and lost one, had one the year before, and two in her first year of "yeaning" and reared them both'. At lambing time farmers lived with their flocks; they saw them last thing at night, often after midnight, and saw them again at five o'clock in the morning, whatever the weather. Indeed the worse the weather the more assiduous farmers had to be. Ewes mostly lamb easily enough, but there are always those that have to be tended to and the lamb removed by manipulation, with arm well inside the ewe up to the elbow. Lambs sometimes come tail first, or all four legs together, or die in the womb. Farmers had to learn to be obstetricians. Twins and triplets were, and still are, sometimes a problem as some ewes only acknowledge one lamb and abandon the other. If so, it has to gathered up and put with the ewe in a pen till she takes to it properly. Some ewes reject their lambs, and there are various ways of getting over this. One old way, mentioned by Fitzherbert, was to put the sheep dog in with the ewe and lamb in the pen, thus triggering off the protective instinct.

> If thy ewe have milk and will not love her lamb, put her in a narrow place made of boards a yard wide, and put the lamb to her and suckle it [help it find the teat] and if the ewe smite the lamb with her head, bind her head with a hay rope to the pen, and if she will not stand, then give her a little hay and tie a dog by her, that she may see him and this will make her love her lamb shortly.

There was also the time-honoured way of flaying a dead lamb and fixing the skin on a lamb whose mother has died, to deceive a lambless ewe in to thinking the lamb is hers. Both these ideas work. Ewes recognize their lambs by smell and their own particular bleat. Some folk poured meths on the lamb, about its tail and on the ewes nose and fore parts to conceal the natural smell. There were all sorts of tricks of the trade and a farmer had to know them all.

Sheep suffer from all sorts of diseases and die very easily. In large flocks, pressed together at shearing time, they can die of stress; they easily 'give up' and some say they have an instinct for suicide. Left alone, in wide open spaces with not too many other sheep, they have a natural instinct to survive and will find grazing if it is there, often in a neighbour's field. In the old days the worst disease was scab which has now returned in this country, having been thought to be quite eliminated. It can, in these days, be treated by dipping regularly in an appropriate solution. All the old farmers had was tar and pitch to put on the itchy sore, though some used a mixture of urine, brine, suet and chopped broom flowers, all boiled together. In summer time, unshorn sheep get struck with the fly. This is the blue bottle fly, that lays its eggs in the soiled wool near the tail, or elsewhere where there is blood or matter. These very quickly develop into the most evil maggots which consume the sheep's flesh while it is still living, and eventually kill it. Cutting the wool away and treating with tar was the old way of dealing with this and putting them up on the moors was another, as here the fly does not strike so much. Shorn sheep seldom get struck and keeping their tails clean of muck in the spring is also vital. Sheep needed both leaving alone and constant attention and moving regularly to fresh grass in enclosed lands. 'Sheep should not hear the church bells ring twice in the same field.'

Marshall noted one peculiarity in the treatment of sheep. In Devon and Cornwall they were shorn before they were washed or dipped. Elsewhere it was the other way round. Unwashed wool weighs heavier, but fetches a rather lower price. Washed wool has lost its natural grease, its 'yolk', and the woollen manufacturer had to grease such wool, at least in the old days. Dipping the sheep shorn may have made dipping safer as sheep can drown in a dip especially as they must have their heads submerged briefly. Shearers surely prefer washed wool, as the 'yolk' stings a cut hand unmercifully. Dipping was made compulsory by law in the last century, and to see that the sheep were all dipped the police had to be notified and would turn up at the sheep dipping (plate 25). It too was something of a festive occasion, with a number of neighbours sharing the same dip. The dogs had all to be dipped at the end, they were as full of fleas and ticks as the sheep, and newcomers to dipping were always threatened with immersion. It was a pleasure to see the sheep free of flies and clean and protected after the dip. In the old days sheep were washed in a stream or river, and there are many places called Sheepwash. Later, farmers had small dips built on the farm, filled from a spring or a tap. Dip smelt acrid, but healthy, and till compulsory dipping was abandoned, scab was unknown.

Farmers always had dogs to help them with sheep. Marshall thought the West Country sheep dogs the best he had seen; they 'rendered a pen unnecessary' and worked in just the way they can be seen to do now. They were shaggy, tall on their legs, grizzled, dun-coloured. These would be the old English sheep dog type, hardly seen working today. He also saw a few smoother, black and white dogs that would be the border collie type. He had not seen 'so much sagacity, activity and subordination' in shepherd's dogs anywhere else. Dogs have to have the instinct to work sheep, a sublimated, controlled, hunting instinct, that occasionally gets out of control if two or three dogs get together. A dog, however good, would be shot out of hand by its owner if proved to be a sheep worrier. Some good looking collies have no instinct at all, and will happily lick a sheep's face.

Pigs

Almost every rural household kept a pig. Healthy and omnivorous, they would be encouraged to scavenge in the farmyard and the lanes until they were ready to be fattened. They were happy in a hovel, under the framework of a rick, or in a pile of straw. They had to be rung through the nose or they would rip up any pasture, but given some rough land, pigs would reduce it to a cultivatable state pretty shortly. Pigs are intelligent, know their own interests very well, and are not frightened of human beings. It is said that a cat looks down on a man, a dog looks up to a man, but a pig looks him straight in the eyes! They can certainly be dangerous, and are known to have killed children. One child was put in the pig's pen for a punishment, was forgotten about, and when looked for, all that was left were the nailed boots! So the tale ran.

The old fashioned south-western pigs must have been the descendants of the great numbers of swine that rootled for mast and acorns and roots in the extensive Devon woodland. Devon had more recorded swine herds than any other county. But as woodland receded and became more valuable, and could be cropped regularly, the swine were excluded, as they were destructive of young woodland. The native breed of pig was long, white, thin carcased and high on its legs. It was let out to grass with the cows until it was three years old and then fattened. The way this was done was another proof to Marshall that 'Devonshire husbandry was not of English growth'. They were shut up in a small close hutch, where they ate, dunged and were fed, and were never let out, or given straw to lie on. They lay in a bed of mud and got covered 'with a thick coat of mail'. This was not idleness on the farmers part. 'Fat pigs should lie wet, it keeps them cool; if they lie on dry warm litter it melts their fat.' Nor should they waste food and energy moving about! Their food was barley meal and potatoes, boiled. This kind of fattening was practised till recently and produced the fat bacon, with no lean, so beloved of Devonians.

14.
The Farmyard

FARMERS LIKED TO HAVE THEIR livestock, their waggons and carts, and their implements close to the house, if possible. So, almost invariably, the farmyard backs or fronts the farmhouse according to the lie of the land. There were in the past no genteel thoughts about keeping animals and muckheaps away from the house. They were part of the farmer's life and work and the nearer the cattle sheds and stables were the better. To separate work from life was unthinkable for a real farmer.

On big farms there was, however, a need for buildings away from the farmhouse. Linhays were built in the remoter fields. These had a loft or talat above, and an open shed with mangers below. They provided shelter and a feeding place for stock, and a storage place for hay, straw, and roots which were harvested nearby. The stock often had the run of some steep rough ground for exercise. The dung from these detached linhays fertilized nearby fields. This saved a great deal of laborious carting of dung and hay from the farmyard, which might lie at one end of the farm down in the combe.

Small farms had less need for detached buildings, so everything was concentrated in the farmyard or the court. This was built so that animals could be kept within gates if need be, and was therefore in a square or oblong with the backs of the buildings built often into the side of the hill to allow for easy loading and unloading. The yard had often two or three entrances, one out onto the public road, one out to the fields, and a narrow gate to the backlet of the farmhouse. Some farms had quite enclosed courts, perhaps to prevent theft and occasionally there was a pair of big gates at the entrance. In the past some big farmers even had some sort of gatehouse, for show perhaps, and protection. John Letheren, a man of moderate wealth, had a gate chamber, and an inner gate chamber at his house at Winkleigh in 1646, and the elaborate Tudor gatehouse at Bradstone fronts what is now no more than a large barton farmhouse. Generally, however, West Country farmhouses and farmyards give little impression of a need for security; moated houses, common in East Anglia, are almost unknown.

Round the farmyard, or court, or mustedge, were a whole variety of buildings. First and foremost on biggish farms was the threshing barn. In Devon, harvested corn was most commonly housed inside, not stacked in a mow or rick. Colpresse says 'we house all'. Except in the South Hams, corn probably took second place to livestock on most farms, though every farm would grow some for home consumption and for sale. Such corn as was grown could be stored in the ends of the threshing barn. This was commonly the biggest building on the farm, often with a fine timbered roof of great age, dating back in some cases to the fifteenth century. This had doors facing each other in the middle of the long sides, to enable packhorses, and later wagons, to unload under cover, and enter and leave easily. The tithe barn at Buckland Abbey, one of the biggest barns in the South West, had doors only wide enough to admit packhorses in 1796, and these had to be widened, with some difficulty, under William Marshall's management, to admit wagons. Ordinary barns on farms must have been altered in the same way when wagons became prevalent. Before that, packhorses unloaded on to the floor of the barn and the sheaves were stacked by prang or pitchfork, however big the barn was. In the space between the two doors, and on either side of it, was the threshing floor where during the winter the sheaves were thrown down to be 'drashed' as needed. Both doors would be kept open during threshing to allow the breeze to take off dust, and even save a bit of icy, hill-top winnowing. Small farmers had no specialized barns like this but used an upper floor to store corn, and a hard earth, or lime ash floor in a doorway for threshing.

In the corn-growing South Hams most farms had a 'corn chamber' near the barn, and numbers of ricks about the farm. John Elliot of South Milton had thirteen ricks on his 188 acres in 1824, and a lot of barley and wheat in the barn and cornchamber. This was a purpose-built, upper-story granary, with a rat and mouse proof 'chamber' approached by a good set of outside stone steps. Up these, the sacks of corn were carried on men's backs, often in sacks weighing $2\frac{1}{4}$ cwt. Men vied with each other to carry such loads, and many suffered ruptures as a consequence! The floor of the chamber was well planked or 'planched', and well plastered where it joined the walls to exclude vermin. It was reinforced underneath with small struts to carry heavy weights. There was often a little window at the peak of one gable end to enable barn owls to swoop silently on mice and rats. Below, at ground level, was a shed where corn could be sacked off through a shoot from the floor above. These attractive corn chambers are common on South Hams farms but rare elsewhere in Devon. They kept the corn dry and secure. Much bigger granaries, built on pillars or on staddle-stones, can be seen in the courts of bigger houses and farms occasionally.

By the late eighteenth century, the bigger farms were using horse power to drive simple machinery. The first device was probably a great granite wheel that rolled vertically in a circular trough to crush apples for cider. This needed nothing but the pull or horses harnessed to a beam. Another use was for horses to turn a machine, something like a capstan, pulling bars

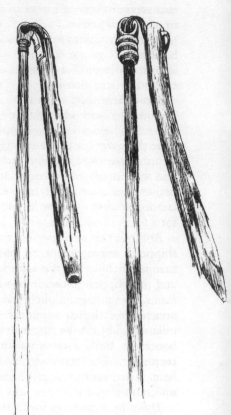

Fig. 32. Two Devon threshing flails. The beating section was made from holly.

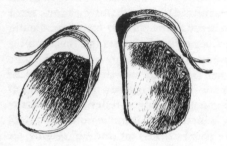

Fig. 33. Leather ox shoes. A pair was needed for each of the cloven feet of the oxen.

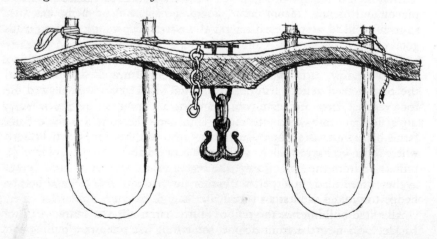

Fig. 34. Double ox yoke

that rotated above the level of their backs. This had a central wheel geared to machinery, either to thresh corn or crush apples, or do a variety of other jobs. Horses walked round and round to do this, hence the name 'round house', though the building itself was not round but pentagonal, built against the wall of a barn. The idea may well have come from the ship's capstan, where men heaved on the bars to haul in the anchor.

Some farms had their own mills, leading water through leats along a contour across meadows, and sometimes, by means of 'launders' (wooden water channels raised on legs) across roads or small valleys to the farmyard. Here there was a mill wheel, which ground corn or turned a thresher. On Mr Venn's farm at Payhembury in 1809 was a wheel which ground, threshed, and winnowed corn, crushed apples and shelled clover seed. These round houses and water wheels were expensive, and were perhaps financed by the landlord rather than the tenant. Some threshed the neighbours' corn too, for a fee.

Around the court were other buildings. Milking cows occupied the shippon, where they were tied up and fed from the talat above into a manger. Behind this was a feeding passage. Cows quickly learnt their stalls, and the shippon seldom housed more than half a dozen cows, even on big farms, in the past. Bullocks and young stock often ran loose in the yard attached to a linhay adjoining the court. These often had attractive round pillars to support the upper floor (plate 5). With round pillars a throng of boisterous bulling cattle could less easily dislodge stonework, or injure themselves. The talat above held hay and straw and farm servants often slept here. The word talat is unique to the South West and its origins are uncertain, but it may be Celtic.

The other buildings for livestock in the court were simple calving sheds, loose boxes where cows could be isolated; a few small sheds for calves and young stock; an ox house in the old days of ox ploughing, much like a shippon; and a stable where horses were groomed and fed and harnessed, again with a talat above where the young horseman or carter might sleep near to his charges. Built into the walls of the buildings sometimes were 'culver' holes, pigeon holes, just big enough to take the domesticated pigeon and its nest. Manor houses had full-scale round dove houses with, so it was said, a nest to each acre of the estate. The young pigeons made good eating.

One peculiar building, six foot square with a low roof and a low door and no window, can sometimes be seen in the farmyards. This was where the pigs were fattened, lying in their own muck and never allowed out for exercise. The most common name for a pig house in Devon was a pig's 'loose', from which the familiar surname Luscombe derives. Some farms had ash houses (there are still several to be seen on Dartmoor), and where roots were grown there would be a root cellar, below ground level for protection from the frost. Roots were otherwise stored in great piles, 'caves' as they were called, in a sheltered corner covered with bracken and browse, hedge trimmings, and straw (plate 20).

All these buildings were grouped in the court. By the entrance to the backlet, and near the front door of the farmhouse too sometimes, was an upping stock or mounting block of stone with some steps, the top just at stirrup level. Before the days of the carriage and farmer's trap, wives and daughters went visiting to market or to church either riding pillion behind their men, or riding on their own mount, side-saddle. Encumbered by long skirts it was probably impossible to 'get aboard' without an upping stock. Another necessity in the court was a large covered water cistern, kept filled from a spring and overflowing into an open drinking trough. In the middle of the court was the dungheap, sometimes in a specially built pit or under a roof. The farmyard was always busy with cows and calves bellowing, roosters crowing and hens fussing their chicks, ducks and geese on the pond, turkeys gobbling and galinies uttering their unbearable machine-like screech. Cats moused, dogs barked and pigeons cooed. The yard was a townplace for animals; no wonder artists found it exciting enough to paint again and again.

Lonely farms needed good guards. Sometimes near a back door was a goose house, rather like a kennel, which held the gander that warned of strangers around, and hissed frighteningly at all callers. All farms kept a number of dogs for protection, bandogs as they were called, as well as sheep dogs, but few had proper kennels and these all slept under a cart ready for work or action at any time. They were often chosen for their fierce tempers. Strangers would be met by a snarl of dogs and unwelcome callers were soon seen off. Before the last century there was no police force to call for protection, so lonely farms needed a fierce dog or two.

Until the last century most of the farm buildings would have been made of cob and roofed with thatch. They were unplastered, so that they were the same colour as the earth from which they were built. Stone was certainly used where it was cheap and plentiful, but to construct in stone required specialist skills, whereas cob buildings were put up by the farmer and his men, or with the help of neighbours. Such buildings would have been made by rule of thumb, with no plans and minimal foundations, and probably looked that way. By the late eighteenth century, when landlords were taking a much closer interest in the working of their farms, it seems that one other thing they did was to remove the responsibility for the house and buildings from the tenant. So it is that on some farms, fine stone buildings with brick coins and slate roofs can be seen. These are almost certainly landlords' work, and they stand out as such, with their hard rectangular outlines, very different from the old rounded peasant style of the more distant past. Today's buildings, prefabricated concrete, steel and asbestos seem quite alien.

Part III: Farm Life

15.
The Family and the Farm

TO MANY, ONE OF THE attractions of country life is continuity, the image of a family settled on the ancestral holding from generation to generation, familiar with their land in a way that only immemorial knowledge, passed on from father to son, could bring. There are a few families in the South West who have held their land for three or four centuries, and one or two, the Seccombes of Seccombe, the Reddaways of Reddaway, who take their names from their farms. A century ago there were surely many more. In Europe generally men felt a great desire 'to keep their name on the land', on a particular farm and went to great lengths to prevent it leaving the family. But so far as it has been studied, this impulse to stay in the same place, come what may, seems to have been very much the exception in the South West, at least in the more recent past.

At a time of rising prices for land it was usual for farmers to move quite happily from farm to farm, as they became more prosperous, or as their family grew, or as they grew older and wished to take on less. Often a death amongst kinsfolk, an inheritance, gave them an opportunity to take a bigger farm, and they did not hesitate to do so. In most parishes there were small, usually rented, farms that were a recognized step up the farming ladder. Men did not move too far, very rarely out of the county, most commonly no farther than the next parish or so, where they would understand the farming and have relations and contacts. Farmers commonly married farmers' daughters, girls who knew their way around the farm and the farm kitchen, and they would have a share in their family's farm eventually, and this too might prompt a move. Until this century, most farmers were tenants and could be forced to move by their landlords. On great estates there were generally suitable farms to let that could accommodate the needs of an ambitious man with growing family. Large farmers who owned their land might hold it for generations, but they were exceptional.

This does not mean that there was no feeling for the land. A man's greatest wish was probably to see all his sons in farms and his daughters married to farmers, and he would seize any opportunity to rent or buy land for his family. It was important for the family to survive and flourish, to farm and to work the land. That was the life they knew, 'a mans life'; no other life was 'real life' in the way farming was. Townsfolk were to be pitied, their work perhaps necessary but disparaged. When Plymouth and London folk were bombed out in the last war, one reaction among country people was to judge them foolish to live in cities anyway.

One son, not necessarily the eldest, inherited the farm his father held when he died; other sons had to be found farms somehow. Some men were content to work as a labourer on another man's farm, or as a 'hind', a bailiff, elsewhere, for years until father died. There was no disgrace for a small farmer's son in working as a labourer; the gap between small farmer and labourer was not nearly so distinct or wide in the South West as it was elsewhere. It was common for a man to hold a bit of land and work for another as well, and many prosperous farmers had started life as labourers. Money made from rabbit trapping, for example, was a good way to get a foot on the farming ladder. Sons inherited when father died, but it was common for women to run the farm if the son was too young or incapable and they often knew the job as well as their husbands. It was also common for sons to take over control of the farm by agreement when father got old and father would move to a smaller farm, or a cottage, or to another part of the house even. Sons were not prevented from marrying until after father and mother died, as they were in Ireland and elsewhere. Room was made for both families in the house and mother-in-law and daughter-in-law just had to get on. Providing for all the children was a problem. Daughters had to have their share somehow, and the inheriting son was often burdened with annuities to be paid to various relations. There was frequently a great web of kin which had claims. In particular, father and mother had to be assured of an income from the farm for as long as they lived.

The burdens of kinship and inheritance were keenly felt in the north Devon village of Northlew in the 1950s, as described by W. M. Williams in his book *Ashworthy*. It was then a remote parish of small farms on rather poor land. There had been a great estate in the parish but this had been sold years before and the farms were mostly owner-occupied. Many had changed hands frequently, particularly since the end of the war, and the attitudes described were those of men who for the most part had bought their farms this century. What was true of the attitudes of the farmers of that particular part of north Devon, however, may not have been the case for other parts of the county, where farms were bigger and more fertile and perhaps employed more labour and needed more capital, and where as a consequence movement from farm to farm was less easy.

From the end of the eighteenth century until the time of First World War, most farmers in the South West were tenants holding their land on seven, fourteen or twenty-one year leases from a landlord. There was no automatic renewal of leases and farming families had no security beyond the length of their lease, and so were unlikely to become attached to any particular farm. A need or wish to farm on a bigger scale when a family was growing up or on a smaller scale when the farmer was nearing retirement might involve a move to another farm. This could be in the same parish on the same estate or might involve taking a fresh farm at some distance. A landlord with good tenants with likely sons might willingly renew the lease, and in bad times was probably glad to have any tenant at all, but there was no guarantee of security. Attachment to particular farms is unlikely in these circumstances.

In contrast, in earlier times there may have been greater security of tenure and farms may have passed from father to son and grandson fairly readily. Up to the middle and end of the eighteenth centuries most farms were leased for three named lives or ninety-nine years, whichever was the shortest. Farming families might look forward to some security, through possibly three generations, sixty or seventy years or more if all the 'lives' lived out their expected term. It was also possible to add a 'life' to the three at a recognized purchase price and thus secure an even longer tenure of a particular farm, so that the farm in fact more or less belonged to a family. Such families were virtual freeholders, and the farm became a real family farm with generations of family memories and associations. The house and buildings were built to the farmer's own design and at his expense. Some men were able to buy their freeholds from their landlord and became true freeholders, and then their land was fully their own and families could stay put in one place.

In many parishes there were freeholders of a different sort, holders of farms that had always been freehold except that they owed a nominal attendance at the manor court and the offering of some recognition of lordship to the lord of the manor, like a rose or a capon on a fixed day. These men often took their names from their farms: Seccombe of Seccombe; Morshead of Morshead; Reddaway of Reddaway; Cholwich of Cholwich; and their forbears may have held the land for centuries since they first cleared and farmed it. Here attachment to the land was strong but not so strong as to prevent the buying and selling of fields or even the move to better land away from the original estate that gave the family its name, often with a rise in status from yeoman to gentleman.

Marriage

Most farmer's sons married farmer's daughters. This was firstly just practical common sense; the new wife had a vital part to play in the running of the farm so she had to know the work. She would move from one farm kitchen to another and do the familiar work her mother and brought her up to do. Before the days of cars few men and girls went very far afield to find a partner; going to market or to the local fair was the great opportunity to make acquaintance outside the parish. On market days the whole family rode into town, father to buy and sell or merely observe prices; son to look at the girls and listen to father's wise words and learn a few tricks of the market; wife to sell her butter and cream and poultry and daughter to look at the boys and help her mother. Here matches might be made and men and girls began to keep company and walk out. Meeting in this way meant that few folk were total strangers or came from far away. In the village of Slapton in the South Hams in 1851, half the population had been born in the village, a fifth more came from the three nearest parishes, and all but a very few of the rest came from the South Hams as a whole; none came from north Devon and only fifteen of the 700 had been born outside the county.

Thomas Tusser gave fairly familiar advice on marriage

> Though love be on choosing far better than gold
> Let love come with somewhat the better to hold.

Most farmers' daughters had some claim to a share in father's property, so that was a consideration in their marriage prospects, and it was not uncommon for living-in labourers or hinds to marry the farmer's daughter and take on the farm. Romance was clearly tempered by more prosaic considerations in this tale from north Devon. Two brothers were marrying two sisters, a double wedding. Tongue tied and shy, they all four failed to point out to the parson, until it was too late, that he had paired them off wrongly. When he knew, he was overcome, but one brother, after some consultation, said reassuringly, 'Don't 'ee worry, passon, us'll bide where us be'. History relates that both marriages were happy and fruitful!

Children

It was important to have sons and daughters to carry on the family to farm the land, and also to care for the parents in old age as they in their turn had almost certainly looked after their parents. This was a great consideration; childless farming couples often had a hard time of it in old age. It was always said that a man would not marry a girl until he knew she could have children. Certainly the registers show that many country brides were pregnant at marriage, but there were also childless marriages to discount this idea. There could be penalties for 'immorality'. Where the parson and the local code was strict, men and girls often of quite good families and well and truly married, but who had obviously 'anitcipated' marriage, or girls who had 'fallen', could be made to do penance by the Church Courts. Penance might involve the unfortunate girl standing before the altar during Matins dressed in a white sheet, barefooted, with hair unbound, and confessing her sins in public. Penance like this was still being imposed in the last century.

Children were much desired and needed to work the farm, but many died very young. Tombstones often reveal the deaths of much-loved boys and girls of five or six. In Slapton, in the early nineteenth century, one in six of the children born died before they were ten, and this was nothing unusual. Most families must have experienced the death of a child. Children born deformed or 'simple' were kept at home, somewhat concealed from the world, as this was easy on a farm, and there was often work they could manage. When children were very small could be the hardest working time for a man who had to manage without much help just when he was starting. If father was still living on the farm, this would be much easier. Girls often went back to mother's house for their first babies and both boys and girls were kept in long clothes as babies until they were three or so when the boys were first 'tucked' into their long clothes, and then 'briched' (put into breeches), an occasion that was remembered. Then they were little men and were expected to begin to learn about farming, following father about getting in the cows, scaring birds and later doing boys' jobs like harrowing or rolling with a horse, or leading a packhorse out for a load of roots. Sons to help meant a much easier time for father.

There was no question of their not working, and no thought of any other job. This was their education for life, far more useful than formal education at school which was just 'book larning' and thought pretty well useless for the life they would lead, as indeed it was in a narrow sense. However, most farmers of any status could read or write by the eighteenth century, though their wives often could not; boys and girls learnt farm work and house work by copying and observation not by formal instruction. They went to market with father, who commented on every price and every animal, and there were secrets to impart, remedies and cures and even charms, not for strangers' ears. If sons went to market they were expected to know who had bought what, from whom and at what price; and if folk could not read or write, they often had exact memories. One quite illiterate man was able to tell his boss all the bids and bidders, and all the prices for all the animals, at yesterday's market without a note. Sons and daughters learnt the work in this way, and often learnt a love for it as well, but there were some, offered no other option, who hated the work all their life.

Relations and neighbours

Even if farmers did not farm the same land for ever, they did not often move far away. Even in the great emigration from Devon in the mid nineteenth century, when hundreds of thousands left, most of the emigrés were probably labourers, and not farmers. Their motive was to find better jobs, at better wages; those in Devon were the lowest paid in the country. Farmers, however, could tighten their belts a bit and survived quite well, even in the depths of the agricultural depression after 1870.

So farmers' families stayed put and were bound therefore to have a whole host of relations who lived not too far away, a web of kindred usually well known to them. In *Ashworthy*, W. M. Williams refers to one couple in the village who could number and name some 240 relatives, most of whom lived within reach; and a dozen other couples could reckon at least 150. One man knew of all the members of seven generations of his family, backwards and forwards, and could construct a huge family tree. Having, and knowing, a host of relations was a matter of pride and an endless source of conversation. The whole countryside might be seen in terms of forbears, grandparents, cousins and second cousins who lived in this or that farm, or had lived there once in the past.

Kin were useful. It was possible to make claims on kin that could not be made on mere neighbours, claims such as help at harvest and the sharing of expensive machinery, and first access to the services of a contractor if he was a cousin. Kin would also lend a young man money when he began to farm on his own, and keep a good eye on him to see that he did nothing foolish. They might give him choice of livestock before they sold at market, and there was a whole range of services that could be claimed in this way on the understanding that they would somehow be returned. Widows with farms and young families were helped in this way too.

Until recent times, farmers tended to steer clear of borrowing from banks; relations were safer, though they would not help if a man was headed for bankruptcy. Farmers, notoriously, had no money in the bank though they may be rich men. In the old days retired farmers acted as a bank, lending money all over the county. In 1696 George Good, a yeoman of Stoke Canon, had £424 lent out all over Devon from Barnstaple to Dartmouth, often in quite small sums. This was out of a total estate of £904. It was a total unwillingness to go to the bank, a lack of nearby kin to whom to leave the farm and approaching old age that prompted the terrible tragedy of the Luxtons at Winkleigh, recorded recently in the book *Earth To Earth*. To have no heir took much of the point out of farming life. Young farmers were told: 'Farm as though you'll live for ever, live as though you'll die tomorrow'!

Much social life revolved around visits to and from relations (when work was not too demanding), attending weddings, funerals and christenings, meeting in church or chapel, and entertaining at Christmas. Jarvis Fairweather, a young farmer at Slapton whose diary survives for 1814, did most of his extensive visiting and receiving of visitors in November and December. He went to Kingsbridge and Totnes to see relatives and in-laws, often staying the night.

Neighbours fulfilled the same function as relatives though the tie was much less close and the claims had to be ones that could be reciprocated fairly easily. Neighbours came in to help with the work, lent or shared machinery, and partook of the harvest and threshing dinners. They would help in an emergency and tolerate straying stock on the assumption that theirs would stray one day too. Some men were totally independent however, and their attitude was 'I want no help, I won't give it'. On being told that his sheep had broken into his own cornfield by a neighbour the response one man gave was 'My sheep, my corn'! Most neighbours co-operated unless there was a real feud, but it is a mistake to think that social life in the parish was necessarily harmonious. Some villages were rent by awful feuds, mostly about nothing much, but stirred up by those who liked to quarrel. Generations had to die out before they ended and often before then the cause was long forgotten. Such feuds were exceptional; most villages probably lived in reasonable harmony allowing for a good deal of sharpish comment and gossip, and a too intimate knowledge of other people's affairs to be entirely comfortable.

In the old days, certain behaviour, such as shrewishness, quarrelling, stand-offishness, showing off, pretentiousness, extravagance, supposed adultery and immorality, and just plain unpopularity were thought intolerable and were dealt with in the traditional way. This was known in

Dorset as the Skimmington or Skimmity ride and in Devon as a Stag Hunt. In Lew Trenchard a notice was posted advertising a meeting of Lord Folkstaff's hounds and these 'met' outside the offenders' house. These offenders were a carpenter and his young wife who dressed too well. A man dressed in cowhide and wearing horns was chased by men and boys and a huntsman in scarlet, horns were blown, kettles and saucepans rattled and finally the 'stag' was brought down on the victims' doorstep and a bladder of blood poured over the threshold. Sometimes the victim had to endure a back-to-front donkey ride. Baring-Gould knew of a good many examples of this in his day and they continued here and there after the First World War. The police would not interfere even when they knew in advance. Worse things occasionally happened, unpopular people without friends or kin disappeared or were 'found drowned', and old women living alone were still in this century thought of as witches in some way, and might be abused. There was at least one accepted use of mercy killing. Victims of rabies, not uncommon in England in the nineteenth century, were smothered 'officially' by the local constable and medical man. In Charlotte Brontë's *Shirley* the heroine was bitten by a dog and asks not to be smothered if she succumbs to rabies. Rabies was known to be incurable and the end frightful, so it was mercy indeed, but nonetheless was legally murder. There are records of this practice going back to the sixteenth century.

The household

Farmers and their families might sit down twelve or so to eat their dinner every day. This would be on fair-sized farms, but even a man with sixty acres would need two or three to help him work the farm and like as not the mistress had a girl or two in the house as well. There were no less than twenty-one 'in the family' on Mr Smallridge's farm of 230 acres at Bridford around 1810, and five of these were parish apprentices, bound by indentures to work for anything up to fourteen years to learn the 'mysteries' of husbandry or housewifery. The remaining sixteen or so would have been paid servants and members of an extended family, with three or more generations all living together in the large farmhouse. Old folk had often reserved for themselves some rooms, food, and a place by the fire, for as long as they lived. In this kind of family there was no problem of what to do with mother when she was widowed and old, or of how to find babysitters for the children. There were sure to be some members of the 'family' at home to tend to the old and the very young. On lonely farms it was too dark in winter to go out much of an evening, and all the hours of the day in summer were occupied with work that could not be put off.

Apprenticing children to farms was common in the South West. It was the ordinary way of dealing with unwanted children, bastards, 'hedge children' and orphans as well as the children of many labouring families. These were the responsibility of the parish, and the parish apprenticed them to local farmers for good or ill. They became the responsibility of the farmers to clothe, feed, and teach their trade; they got no wages, and their only recourse if they were badly treated was to appeal to the parish or to a magistrate. Farmers got virtually free labour, more or less slave labour, to treat as they liked and they were stuck with apprentices for as long as their term lasted. It says something for farmers that labourers who had themselves been apprenticed chose to apprentice their own children in their turn, because they believed that that offered them the best chance. Labourers, of course, did not have much choice; on their dismal wages, they could do little else if they had a large family. But at its best life for an apprentice child in the farmer's household was good. Apprentices sat down to table with the farmer and his children and ate the same food, they 'lived much better than at home', 'there was always wheaten bread ready', 'plenty of meat and drink'. They slept in the sons' or daughters' rooms and seem to have been treated in the same way as the farmer's children.

Mrs Tuckett, who farmed near Dunsford around 1840, described how she treated child workers. 'My house is conducted in the old fashioned Devonshire way, myself the servants and apprentices all get meals together and all have the same things.' They were not allowed out after seven, they were forbidden to go to fairs and wakes that were 'so dangerous to girls'. On Sundays she taught them to read and to say their Catechisms and prayers, as the Sunday school was too far away, and they had to tend the cattle, Sunday or no Sunday. If they earned a bit of money from visitors, holding horses and so on, she saved it for them for when they left. She gave them a certificate of good conduct when they left, and five days holiday at Easter and Christmas. Their parents could come to see them, and could have a meal, and there were 'amusements' provided occasionally. She kept the boys and girls strictly apart both at work and in the house and she made a point of 'looking after them herself' and tried to keep the girls away from work on the land where they could not be supervised. Her apprentices came back to see her in after life, and she kept an eye on all their careers. Mrs Tuckett ran the farm herself after her husband died as did many farmers' widows, and related with pride that all six apprentices chose to stay with her, though they could have been 'bound' elsewhere.

Mrs Tuckett was clearly a firm and motherly mistress, but there were some brutal employers. Mr Troode of Exminster occasionally took the whip to cheeky girls; he was fined for this by a magistrate and resolved never to have any more apprentices. He prefered servants, who could be instantly fired, while apprentices had to serve their time out. He accused apprentices of arson, neglecting livestock, and wanting pay they were not entitled to, and so on. Not half his apprentices turned out well, he said. He complained of a boy that absented himself from church; the boy got whipped and sent to the treadmill for this misdemeanour.

Mary Puddicombe, a labourer's wife, remembered being beaten black and blue, 'but not much hurt' by the master, and knew of a girl who had her arm cut to the bone with a stick cut from the hedge by the young master, for not harrowing evenly. But she also remembered eating well, helping herself to the bread and cheese when she liked, and she sent her own children as apprentices to very good places. Above all, she remembered the work. In later life she worked as a washerwoman and said that washing was harder than farm work. She was employed 'driving bullocks to field, cleaning their houses, bedding them up, washing potatoes and boiling them for pigs, milking', leading horses or bullocks to plough ('maidens would not like that work now'), mixing lime and earth, digging potatoes, pulling turnips in the snow, reaping a little, loading packhorses, going out with a horse to cut furze, getting up at five or six, (three o'clock on market days), and going to bed at half past nine. When she complained of a beating to her parents, they told her 'to be a better maiden next time'. Mr Troode complained that 'when girls are getting up to be girls, some smart girl will make them ashamed to feed pigs, and girls must feed pigs'!

Thomas Tusser found servants equally difficult to deal with, girls particularly, to whom he gave the name 'fizzgigs'. They were always running off to the mill to gossip, or chattering, or shirking their work; nor were they very clean in his view. No kitchen should have a mirror or they would be for ever primping, and

> Some slovens from sleeping no sooner get up
> But hand in the aumbrie and nose in the cup!

He recommended the stick. 'Let holly wand threat, let fizzgig be beat.' He did, however, recognize good servants:

> Some servants are oftenest painful and good
> That sing at their labours as birds in a wood.
> These good servants hope justly some friendship to feel,
> And look to have favour what time they do weel.

At best, on small farms, servants and apprentices became part of the family.

16.
Society and Religion

Village business

In many parishes society was dominated by the squire, who might own almost all the land and live in the manor house. He would almost certainly be a Justice of the Peace and preside at Petty Sessions where local offences were tried. He would, with his fellow Justices, have 'governed' the county until the county councils were established in 1889. In the parish his word was law; few decisions could be made without his approval. He was landlord, and the parson was perhaps his cousin and would very likely be his appointee; they thought alike and came from the same class. The lesser folk deferred to them, and though the village looked after its own roads, tended to its own poor, maintained a 'poor house', appointed constables to look after law and order, the deciding influence would be the squire's.

Fortunately or unfortunately, many parishes had no squire. Either the land had many owners or the squire was an absentee and administered his estates through an agent or steward. These villages then had very largely to administer their own affairs themselves. Most men preferred to live in an 'open' village where the land was not all in one man's hands, and where they could live much as they liked without being aware of, or beholden to, the squire or his lady.

Farmers had in these circumstances an important role to play in the community. The bigger farmers were the richest folk in the village, they were accustomed to making decisions; some, as freeholders or large leaseholders, might have the vote. They would have some knowledge of, or contact with, 'polite society' and 'trade' in the nearest town, or in the larger centres, such as Exeter or Bodmin or Barnstaple. They, together with the smaller farmers and tradesmen of the village, found themselves saddled with the responsibility of local village government.

There were a variety of jobs to be done. If they were Anglicans they would almost certainly take it in turns to be churchwardens. This job involved the care of the fabric of the church and its yard and interior; raising money to do this from a parish rate or by other means; looking after the church house, the parish hall of the old days; seeing that the church bells were in order and well hung and sounded, not only on Sundays, but on special occasions of celebration such as a great victory or the birth of an heir to the throne. They had many lesser jobs: they had to keep vermin down in the parish by paying trappers, or paying a bounty on heads or tails of crows, badgers (mistakenly thought of as vermin) or foxes. Any poor travelling strangers who passed through the village, such as shipwrecked sailors, or released prisoners of the Turks or the French on their way home, had the right to temporary sustenance from the parish if they had a magistrate's pass. All this expenditure came out of church rates. They had, further, to make a return every year to the archdeacon on the state of the church, and look after all the parish documents. If the parson was suspect in his religious views, or an ill-liver, or totally incompetent, the churchwardens might report him to the bishop. Almost certainly they would be involved in any school in the parish, in the appointment of a schoolmaster, and in the administration of any village charity.

Raising money was always a problem. Parishioners were by law compelled to pay a church rate, assessed largely on land and fixed at an agreed sum. The churchwardens had to work out what was needed for the next year and assess how many church rates had to be raised and then collect them. There were other ways. Some parishes kept a flock of sheep. Each farmer took so many parish sheep and the lambs and the wool went to the parish. Similarly the churchwardens might stage a 'church ale'. Two of them, or any group of parishioners, would brew a great vat of ale and sell it at a village party in the church house, and the profits would go to the church. The Puritans largely put a stop to this useful enterprise. 'Church ales' explain why so many church houses became pubs eventually, and why here and there parishes still own the 'local'. At the end of the year the churchwardens had to render an account. All this was quite responsible work and it was taken seriously. Clearly one of the wardens, or particularly the parish clerk, had to be literate and numerate, and they had to work in close association with the rector which may not always have been easy. They were responsible for fair sized funds and had to account for them.

Much the same was true of the overseers of the poor. Every parish was bound to look after its poor, and there were always orphans, the sick, the improvident and some elderly folk who could not look after themselves. Parishioners were obliged to pay a 'poor rate' which had to be assessed in advance from year to year; it was collected, of course, not without difficulty. Funds then had to be distributed, and this was done in a variety of ways. People in need of help would apply to the overseers who would assess their case. All the village folk and their circumstances would be well known and local men were often in a good position to judge their needs accurately and fairly. It was probably an unenviable job, carrying with it a good chance of being accused of favouritism or neglect.

The parish may have maintained a 'poor house', where those who could not look after themselves were housed, and the running of this would be the overseers' responsibility. They would have to decide whom to take in and whom to refuse. Poor people living at home would have to be clothed and allowed a sum to feed themselves. If they were sick, the parish paid someone to look after them, and when they died their funerals had to be paid for too. Child apprentices were bound by the parish, a responsibility falling to the overseer and the churchwardens. A good man would keep an ear open to see that children were not badly treated. Perhaps the most difficult job was to keep an eye on newcomers to the parish, to see if they were likely to become a burden on the poor rate, through sickness, poverty or the necessity of supporting a large family. Such folk were often turned away and not allowed to settle in the parish unless their own parishes agreed to have them back if need arose. Settlement was a great problem. The parish had no obligation to support anyone who did not have a settlement, a right to live in the parish, and this depended on a variety of circumstances, place of birth, place of last work and so on. Parishes disputed with one another about settlements, often at great expense in law suits and meetings. That was not the end of it. Illegitimate children were always likely to be a charge on the parish, so the overseer would need to know of such children, and find out the fathers and get them to pay a maintenance.

Some parishes had rough folk to deal with. Families could live very independent, almost lawless lives in some of the remoter combes around Exmoor or off the moors of mid Devon. Registers sometimes record the wholesale baptism of the adults and children of all ages, father, mother and all, who had perhaps escaped the parson's notice for many years. The outlaws of legend, the Doones and the north Devon savages who lived in a cave, are almost certainly mythical. At the time the Doones were said to have lived, Exmoor Forest was ruled by a warden who would not have tolerated them in any way. The poet William Browne wrote of the Gubbins family who had no knowledge of the law off God or Man, lived as savages in a cave, and howled at passers by. They lived somewhere near Lydford on Dartmoor, and were in men's view 'rubbish', as their name now implies. The vast majority of the poor were more civilized than these wild instances, and needed a lot of looking after. There was a great deal of paper work, a great deal of knowing other people's business and making fair assessments. Much of the legal side of the work had to be decided by a JP, but the groundwork was the overseer's business. It may seem doubtful if anyone liked the job of overseer much, and no doubt many farmers thankfully passed the job on to a neighbour at the end of the year. However, some men evidently liked the job and kept it from year to year. It gave a lot of power over other folk, which some might relish; the only check, ultimately, on that power was appeal to the local Justice of the Peace, who appointed the overseers initially. After 1834 the parish was no longer responsible for its poor and the job disappeared, and with it some feeling of communal parish responsibility for known and recognized neighbours.

The remaining parish job was that of overseer of the highways or waywarden. This was a practical matter, keeping the parish roads in order. Once again a rate was raised, and men were employed to carry out repairs. In the past it had been the duty of every parishioner to give so many days work freely on the roads, and provide horse and cart or packhorse if they had them. They had to be persuaded to turn out when needed and that may have been difficult. Poor people 'on the parish' were sometimes employed on the roads also, but latterly, until the county and district councils took over, the parish merely paid folk to do the work.

All these part-time unpaid officials, the churchwardens and the various overseers, as well as the parson, made up the government of the village, the Vestry as it was called, administering national law on a parish scale. These men were the élite of their small community, the richest and most influential and the most powerful. They knew everyone and everyone knew them. They had a concern and interest in village affairs that was taken from them almost entirely in the 1880s, when the new district councils were established. Parish councils of today are a pale imitation of the real local government that preceded them.

Church and chapel

Probably no one knows how well the village church was attended in the old days. A picture of the village assembled, all the pews filled every Sunday, everyone in their rightful place, the squire in his private pew, the better-off at the front, the poor at the back or against the wall, the parson in his pulpit with the parish clerk at his desk below, is delightful but probably inaccurate. Some indication of real committment is suggested by the number of those who took communion; seventy out of a population of around 1000 at Hemyock in 1821 when there were no Dissenting chapels in the parish; 200 out of perhaps 1700 at Hartland; thirty-five out of 700 at Chawleigh and so on. Of course unconfirmed children could not partake, and attendance at Communion may not be a good measure of the ordinary man's interest in the Church. There were pressures to attend; in a 'squired' village tenants ran some risk if they did not appear fairly regularly, and many folk wanted to be seen at church to show they were respectable and part of society. Church was also a good place to make or improve acquaintance, to meet friends regularly and to look out for a future husband or wife.

There were always some enthusiasts. It would be difficult to match that of the small farmer who walked from near Cambridge to Colchester, some fifty miles, to listen to preaching and, dissatisfied with what he had heard, went home and was prepared to go on, on foot, to Oxford to seek Bishop Latimer's views if in the meantime he had not quelled his doubts. That was in the 1550s. From the Reformation there were always those who found the Church of England not to their liking, and met in houses or out of doors, or founded congregations and built chapels, so that they could worship God in their way. Few parishes, from the seventeenth century on, were far from a nonconformist chapel, which might often be in the local town, but sometimes, like Spicelands Meeting House at Uffculme, and Loughwood Chapel in a farmyard near Kilmington, deep in the country. After John Wesley toured Devon and Cornwall there were

Methodist chapels everywhere, notably in the mining areas of Cornwall, built, maintained and financed by local folk, the land often given by a farmer. There were many persuasions among the nonconformists: Primitive Methodist, Plymouth Brethren, Baptists, Quakers and Congregationalists. The history of these last three can be traced back to the seventeenth century, and they suggest that there was always a body of opinion in most villages that both disagreed with the doctrines of the Anglican church, found it deeply unsatisfying spiritually, and resented its claims and pretensions and status.

Devon and Cornwall witnessed one great burst of local religious enthusiasm and independence in the last century, the Bible Christian movement, founded in 1815. The founder of this, William O'Bryan was a Cornish farmer's son, but the best known local preacher, James Thorne, another farmer, came from Shebbear in north Devon, and the movement spread widely from there. Their popularity can be seen from their numerous, rather stark and lonely chapels, often built in corner of a field well away from any other house. Farmers were, and are, the backbone of the Bible Christians, now part of the United Reformed church.

All the chapel people, whatever their persuasion, found the Church of England intolerable. Farmers resented tithe bitterly, the payment of one tenth of their produce every year to the Church, enforced by law. It was often unfairly collected, and sometimes it was paid to absentee laymen, who had bought the right or whose ancestors had acquired it after the Reformation. In Slapton, tithe was paid to the Catholic Lord Arundel who did the minimum to support the Anglican church in the village. Dissenters and nonconformists had to pay it, despite the fact that they worshipped elsewhere and received no benefits from the Church. It was often a source of bitter dispute and the farmers relished cheating the parson of his dues.

> We've cheated the parson, we'll cheat him again
> For why should a blockhead have one in ten?
> For prating so long like a book learned sot
> While pudding and dumpling burn to pot.

Some refused to pay altogether and the bailiffs were eventually sent in to sell them up. At Hemyock one Baptist farming family was sold up in this way two or three times. When the sale took place, the neighbours bought all the stock for minimal prices and restored them to the owner, raising enough from the sale to pay the tithe, and woe betide anyone who tried to out bid them. This family was not alone in their resistance. There were other deeply felt grievances, the obligation to marry and register births and deaths in the church, the fact that many clergy did not serve their parishes, or served two or more and paid a poor curate to do their work, but took all the tithes. Nonconformists were often buried separately 'behind' the church and sometimes they were discriminated against in life. At Iddesleigh the parson refused a near-starving widow parish relief because she 'attended Meetings'. Such 'Meetings' were an ever-present reproach to the parson.

Many parsons were saintly, loving, Christian souls, who cared for their parishioners devotedly. But most of them belonged to the upper or upper-middle class and were 'gentry'. Many condescended and patronized, and assumed the right to decide and direct, speaking of their flock as if the individuals who comprised it did not have minds of their own. Chapel folk, on the other hand, ran their own affairs, and chose, to some extent, their own ministers, and that was attractive to the independently-minded farming folk. This independence spilt over into politics; small farmers and nonconformists were one of the pillars of the Liberal party in the last century in the South West, which was one of its great strongholds. This sentiment still persists to day, though there are fewer small farmers, and nonconformity is less strong. Larger farmers tended to be Anglican, and normally Tory. Their interest in the land coincided with that of their, mostly Tory, landlords.

Some villages were well and truly split by religion though this did not necessarily create animosity. Everyone knew who was 'chapel' and who went to church. Chapel folk did not go to the pub and had strict standards but, unless they were Brethren, that did not prevent them sharing in the village life to the full, running local clubs, and attending all the church and village fêtes and sales of work. However, they probably steered pretty clear of the annual revel which was a fairly riotous occasion, although this had pretty much died out by the early nineteenth century. Families often crossed this religious divide, and the bond of family seems sometimes to have been rather stronger than that of faith. At their worst, chapel folk were censorious, exclusive and not easy to live with; nevertheless there is little evidence of any determined feuding on religious grounds in villages.

It cannot have been easy for an Oxbridge educated, intellectually minded parson to settle in a remote village with only his neighbouring colleague for equal company. Some became eccentrics, some antiquarians, and one printed volumes of his own sermons setting all the type himself. A few took to the bottle, and some took to hunting. Quite a number, Jack Russell of Swimbridge is the best known, had their own packs of hounds and hunted twice a week.

> In pulpit Parson Hogg was strong, he preached without a book sir
> And to the point and never long, and this the text he took sir!
> O tally ho! O tally ho! Dearly beloved, zounds Sir!
> I mount my mare to hunt the hare, singing Tally Ho! the hounds Sir.

Of a good many the tale is told of how they would abandon the service if the hunt passed by, or a fox was spied.

Some parsons were plainly bad men. Froude of Knowstone, with the help of a gang of ruffians, set fire to the ricks of parishioners he did not like, beat his wife, and 'was guilty of every crime in the calendar'. He terrified his parishioners, who said that he had the evil eye. One parson liked to fight, and took on professional prize fighters. The bad ones were remembered and talked about while the good ones are forgotten. Some were 'squarsons', squire cum parson, and wielded immense local power; the Copplestones at Offwell owned the village, lived in the manor house, patronized the school as well as presenting themselves to the living, their own property, for two hundred years. Some were much more down to earth, like Fielding's Parson

Trulliber who was a farmer six days a week and parson the seventh, renting land, feeding pigs, as fat as a pig himself, with a strong country accent. From his name he was a West Country man. Baring-Gould tells a tale of one parson who was invited to stay with the squire for a couple of days, and who spent the next two days equally, or more, at home 'below stairs' with his friend the butler. Folk liked their parsons to be human. The attendance at one parson's church jumped immensely once he had been found drunk in a ditch. What folk could not stand was to be preached at, to be made to feel morally and spiritually inferior to their pastor. A really gentle soul, with no toughness about him, would get cheated. One old song relates with glee how Passon Brown's sheep was stolen for the village Christmas dinner, and he was starved out of the parish. Some hard working men regarded the parson with contempt; a free house, a good stipend and he did no real *work* at all in their view. But folk had to live with the parson, whatever his views and character, he was an institution. For almost everyone who was not 'chapel', the Church had one real function in their lives. There were certain rites of passage that had to be observed: christening, churching, marriage and burial. Folk may have come to church reluctantly and infrequently, but these ceremonies were necessary and important for life. Churching, after the birth of a baby was so important that there was often a special churching pew for young wives. It was thought of as a form off ritual cleansing. These were all social ceremonies that happened to be celebrated in church.

Baring-Gould says that in his youth country people were intensely superstitious, believing in hauntings and 'wishtnesses' and in churchyard ghosts and presences, ghosts haunting cross roads and fords over rivers. Many believed in divination and spells and charms. This is a charm for a scald.

> Three angels came out of the North and East and West.
> One brought fire, one brought ice, and the third brought the Holy
>   Ghost
> So out fire in frost!

Sometimes real pagan instincts came to light. In 1879 Farmer Jonas Squire of Collishaw Farm, Meavy, had a sickness amongst his cattle. He sacrificed a sheep to the 'good folk' and burnt it on the moor behind his house. He did not think he had done anything extraordinary. Baring-Gould thought that these superstitions had all gone in his life time, but there are still white witches to cure warts and not so long ago a charm for a burn was thought to be effective, even if uttered down the telephone.

17.
Fun and Festivals

FARMING PEOPLE DID NOT HAVE much leisure. The pace and demands of the work was set by the seasons and the weather and there was no escaping these. If the hay was fit, it had to be turned; if the soil was fit, seed had to be sown: a day later might be too late. But there were times in the year when nature was not so inexorable. Then farmers liked to visit, and their idea of a good day out was to visit a farming friend and have a look at his livestock and crops, and discuss the oddities of another neighbour's doings. Farmers loved their life and their work. On Sundays the best thing to do was to lean on a gate, look at the stock and make plans for the next week or season.

Farmers liked to give great parties. The guests would be bidden to come early, that meant ten or eleven o'clock in the morning when they had something to eat 'after their journey', then a feast in the middle of the day, all home produced and home cooked, followed by a walk round the farm for the men and a visit to the dairy and a look at the poultry for the women. Then more food and much dancing, lots of cider and often some good smuggled French brandy. Farmer Jarvis Fairweather of Slapton bought his brandy and 'Hollands' at the fishing village of Hallsands, where it could only have been smuggled. That would add spice to the occasion.

There were the other country pursuits. Most farmers had guns and liked to shoot, and the most prized and difficult target was the elusive woodcock. Jarvis Fairweather noted with pride in his diary when he bagged one of those. He was rather lucky to be able to shoot game. He owned his farm but tenants were forbidden by their landlords to shoot game and were only reluctantly allowed to kill rabbits. The shooting was preserved for the landlord's pleasure.

Everyone could hunt and the hunts of the past were in no way exclusive or only for the rich. Most of the south-western hunts were farmers' hunts and anyone who could find some sort of a horse was eligible. At the end of the day the hunters would return home worn out but exhilarated, not by the kill, but by the exercise and effort and risk involved in a twenty mile run over bogs and streams and through woods. It would bear up to Jorrocks' verdict: 'the image of war without its guilt and only twenty-five percent of the danger'.

Killing deer or foxes stirred no qualms of conscience; the deer ate the farmer's turnips and the fox and badger killed his poultry. He would have thought himself a fool to leave them alone, and that destroying them was entirely part of the natural order of things. Countrymen loved hunting; everything would stop on the farm when the hunt passed, and the nearest vantage point was sought to see the tricks of the fox, hear the blowing of the horn and see the skills of the hounds. Foxes were the real enemies and, in the old days, when one was seen and traced, the church bells were rung for everyone to stop work for a day's sport. Foxes were also trapped and dug out; there were even professional fox catchers and fox shoots, and sometimes no love lost between them and the hunt. One enthusiastic fox shooter threw a couple of old dead foxes that he had shot to the hunt to encourage their rather ineffectual efforts. Badgers and polecats and foxes were enemies, vermin, to be fought and destroyed. All dealings with animals, castration, tail docking, slaughter with a pole axe, involved some pain and distress; hunting was hardly different.

These were men's pleasures mainly, but there were gentler ones enjoyed by all. The great event of the year was the local fair held in almost every market town on a fixed and recognized date. All the family went to this and labourers were given the day off and children saved their money for it. Immense business was done, all sorts of travelling traders, chapmen, and pedlars came to the fair. The housewife bought her year's supply of cloam, and 'cheapened' (bargained) for ribbons and cloth; the young men and girls bought each other 'fairings'; there was strange food and drink for sale; all the pubs were open all day and all the neighbourhood from miles around came in to see and be seen. Fair day was a fixed point in folks' minds, to which events and happenings were related. Few country folk went far afield: a visit to the local fair was an event, to Exeter or Truro, Bodmin or Barnstaple an adventure and on to London unthinkable.

Next to the fair in importance came the village revel, also on a fixed day, often the day after the parish church's saints day, or often on Whit Monday. This event was marked more by games than by trade. Great football matches were staged, involving all the young lads of the village, who played all the lads of the next village over fields and moors. Parracombe played Martinhoe, over miles of the open moor that lay between them and the goals were the churchyards in each village. Football often ended in a riot on a small scale. A great attraction was wrestling in the old south-western style, bouts that went on for hours. In Devon men used hardened shoes to hack at their opponents shins. There were famous champions. Cann and Thorne for Devon, Polkinghorne and Warren for Cornwall. Men would travel miles for a purse in well advertised matches. The great aim was to 'show the white horse', that is to throw a man on the flat of his back.

Revels sometimes incorporated relics of ancient ceremonies and rituals. The hobby-horses of Padstow, Minehead and Combe Martin, and the Helston Furry dance all seem to be ancient spring festivals, while the tar-barrel rolling at Ottery St Mary and Torrington on 5 November probably has its origins in winter fire festivals. Carrying a burning tar barrel through the streets was not confined to these places in the old days. At Combe Martin the rebel Irish Earl of Rone (Tyrone) was 'hunted', 'captured', 'shot' and 'drowned' every year, commemorating probably, the part Combe Martin men played in the Irish campaigns of Queen Elizabeth's reign. This became a drunken riot and was in the end suppressed by the parson, though now revived. At Thurlestone great fires were lit on midsummer day 'to celebrate the slaughter of the Danes by the women of the village', after their husbands had been killed and they themselves raped.

Revels often ended up in a fight with a neighbouring village. There were great rivalries, and villages and villagers had nicknames and particular qualities. Some of these feuds, between Chagford and Moretonhampstead for instance, were supposed to derive from the Civil War. It was unwise to say 'Baa' to a Culmstock man, since the last man to be hanged for sheep stealing came, it was said, from there. Most of the attributions are unexplained. Lympstone folk were 'long heads', Mariansleigh people were Marley 'bread eaters', and a mention of mud was enough to enrage a Topsham man. Topsham folk were, it was said, too poor to have doors! A shout of 'Topsham' or 'You're not living in Topsham', was a reminder to close a door. Combe Martin was rudely called Shamwick, as was Bideford East the Water, both at one time dirty industrial settlements.

Attributions of collective characteristics were popular. The rhyme, 'Burrington maids be fair and tall...Bickington maids be dancers all', was current in the eighteenth century, and there must have been many more such definitions. It is possible that the folk from one village often looked a bit alike; in small communities there would be enough inbreeding to fix some characteristics. Mariansleigh men were particularly tall and long-lived, the parson wrote in his reply to Dean Mille's enquiry.

There were many calendar customs to be observed. There was Lent crocking when children pelted front doors with broken crocks for a gift of food. It was accompanied by a song 'Pray dame something, apple or dumpling'; and children would ring front door bells or knock on the door, till the housewife gave in. It was sometimes known as Dappy Door Night. In some places a cock was tied and put under a cloam dish, and stones were thrown till the cloam broke and the cock was killed. On Mothering Sunday, the fourth in Lent, everyone went to visit their mothers and ate 'mothering' cake. On Shrove Tuesday everyone ate pancakes, tossed them over the fire and ate their own, burnt or not. Hot-cross buns, if kept and dried, were good for whooping cough, but no dishes were washed or pigs killed on Good Friday. Easter was a good time for tilling gardens, and shifting bees, and weaning children. On Easter Day some folk got up to see the sun 'dance for joy' and hoped to see the Lamb and Flag outlined in the disc of the Sun.

May was a busy month. On 1 May, Maydoll Pay, girls dressed up veiled dolls and exacted money for a view of the dolls' faces. On the same day the hobby-horses performed their grotesque dances; 2 May was Kissing Day and 3 May was Stinging Nettle Day when children lashed each other with nettles for fun! May was the time for girls to collect rushes for rush lights 'singing a pretty song'. The three days of 17, 18 and 19 May were the icy Franklin nights, after which frosts were unlikely and summer had really come. Some folk built May fires and made their cows walk through the ashes to ensure abundant milk. Oakapple day was next, on 29 May, and in some places Lawless Day, where masters and servants swapped roles, and children splashed passers-by with water from the gutters. At Whitsun girls went in procession in white to the church and some folk beat the bounds of the parish with all the children, to define its identity, perhaps, as well as its physical limits.

The year was full of such ceremonies; hardly a month passed without some custom being observed, if all the accounts are true. Christmas was the end of the farming year when work could stop for twelve days, and the farmer entertained his men and his neighbours, and ate plum porridge and goose; the apple trees were wassaailed and the mummers came round with their farcical plays about St George and the Turk, and any other currently well-known political figure. At Christmas the cattle knelt in the shippon and the robin sang its loudest; the huge ashen faggot was burnt in the hearth, made out of cleft ash branches cut that morning and bound with a withy bind. At each crack of the bind everyone drank, and a brand was carefully put away for next year's Christmas fire, to show that the cycle of life would go on.

Bibliography

Books
(Where known, original and most recent edition are indicated.)

Sabine Baring-Gould *Early Reminiscences, 1834–1864* (Bodley Head, 1923)
Sabine Baring-Gould *Further Reminiscences, 1864–1894* (Bodley Head, 1925)
Sabine Baring-Gould *Old Country Life* (Methuen 1890; EP Publishing, 1975)
Fernand Braudel *The Structures of Everyday Life* (1979; English ed. Fontana, 1985)
Mrs A. E. Bray *On the Borders of Tamar and Tavy* (1836; Kent and Co., 1879)
Richard Carew *Survey of Cornwall* (1602; Andrew Melrose, 1953)
Margaret Cash (ed) *Devon Inventories* (Devon and Cornwall Record Society, 1966)
William Chapple *Review of Risdon's Survey of Devon* (1785)
Veronica Chesher *The Cornishman's House* (Bradford Barton, 1968)
Celia Fiennes *Journeys, 1685–1712* (Macdonald, 1984)
H. P. R. Finberg *Tavistock Abbey* (1951; David and Charles, 1969)
Anthony Fitzherbert *The Book of Husbandry* (1534; English Dialect Society, new edition)
R. Fraser *General View of the County of Devon* (1794; Porcupines 1970)
R. S. Hawker *Footprints of Former Men in Far Cornwall* (John Lane, 1903)
W. G. Hoskins and H. P. R. Finberg *Devonshire Studies* (Jonathan Cape, 1952)
W. G. Hoskins *Devon* (Collins, 1954; David and Charles, 1972)
E. T. MacDermot *History of the Forest of Exmoor* (1911; David and Charles, 1973)
William Marshall *Rural Economy of the West of England* (2 vols, 1796; David and Charles, 1970)

E. W. Martin *The Shearers and the Shorn* (Routledge Kegan Paul, 1965)

Nancy Phelan *The Swift Foot of Time* (Quartet Books, 1985)

Tristram Risdom *Survey of the County of Devon* (1630; Porcupines, 1970)

Robert Trow Smith *English Husbandry* (Faber and Faber, 1951)

W. H. Thornton *Reminiscences of an Old West Country Clergyman* (Andrew Iredale, 1897)

Cecil Torr *Small Talk at Wreyland* (1918; Adams and Dart, 1970)

Thomas Tusser *Five Hundred Points of Good Husbandry* (1580; Oxford University Press, 1984)

Charles Vancouver *General View of the Agriculture of Devon* (1808; David and Charles, 1969)

Thomas Westcote *View of Devonshire* (1630; Roberts, Exeter, 1845)

J. A. C. Whetter *Cornwall in the Seventeenth Century* (Lodenek Press, 1974)

W. M. Williams *A West Country Village: Ashworthy. Family Kinship and Land* (Routledge Kegan Paul, 1963)

Articles

N. Alcock and Charles Hulland: numerous articles in the *Transactions of the Devonshire Association* (*TDA*) between 1968 and 1980 on Devon farmhouses.

C. Ann Baker, 'The origins of South Devon cattle' *Agricultural History Review*, 1984

R. P. Chope 'Some old farm implements and operations' *TDA*, 1918

Christopher Clay 'Life leasehold in the Western counties of England' *Agricultural History Review*, 1981.

H. S. A. Fox 'The field systems of East and South Devon' *TDA*, 1972

A. Jewel 'Some cultivation techniques in the south-west of England' in *Exeter Papers in Economic History*, 14, 'Agricultural Improvements Mediaeval and Modern' (University of Exeter, 1981)

C. H. Laycock. 'The Old Devon Farmhouse' *TDA*, 1920, 1922, 1923

R. G. F. Stanes (ed.) 'A georgicall account of Devon and Cornwall, 1667' *TDA*, 1964

'Devon Agriculture in the Eighteenth Century: the Evidence of the Milles' MS., in *Exeter Papers in Economic History*, 2 'The South West and the Land', (University of Exeter, 1969)

R. G. F. Stanes 'Landlord and tenant and husbandry covenants in eighteenth century Devon', in *Exeter Papers in Economic History*, 14, (see above)